BRIDGES ON THE RIVER WYE

BRIDGES ON THE RIVER WYE

Alan Crow

With drawings by Barbara Crow

LAPRIDGE PUBLICATIONS
1995

First published in 1995 by
Lapridge Publications
25 Church Street
Hereford HR1 2LR

©Copyright 1995 Alan Crow

Alan Crow is hereby identified at the author of this work
in accordance with the Copyright, Designs and Patents Act 1988

ISBN 0 9518589 9 8

Printed in Great Britain by
Biddles Ltd. of Guildford

To Lesley for her never failing
patience and encouragement

CONTENTS

ACKNOWLEDGEMENTS

References to the sources of information are given in brackets at the end of each bridge description, but I should like to thank those who have been particularly helpful and encouraging in response to my enquiries. These include: Keith Kissack whose book *The River Wye* was my first introduction to the river, and who first suggested that the results of my retirement hobby should be published; Stan Coates, authority on the industrial history of the Wye, who introduced me to the records of the Royal Monmouthshire Royal Engineers with valuable results and who has also kindly read the text; Bryan Lawrence of Powys County Library who made his detailed knowledge of the upper reaches of the Wye available to me; J.B. Groucott who gave me details of his studies of 19th century bridges; and Heather Hurley, author of works on roads and bridges in Herefordshire and the Wye Valley, for her encouragement. I should also like to thank the staff of the County Highways Departments at Worcester and Llandrindod Wells, including John Hough in the latter, and of the County Records Offices at Hereford and Llandrindod Wells. I am also happy to acknowledge the technical information on bridge building given to me by Peter Tomlinson of Mabey & Johnson Limited and by Geoffrey Booth of Fairfield-Mabey Limited; and similarly N. Hope of Newbridge-on-Wye and Bernard Lloyd of Rhayader on the footbridges of the upper reaches of the river. I should also like to thank Andrew Helme for helping me with photographs in the Monmouth Museum collection, and Ron Shoesmith of Hereford City Archaeological Unit and Catherine Wilson of the Hereford City Museum, as well as the staff of Hereford Library, for similar help. Above all I am indebted to Tim Pridgeon, not only for editing the text but for ensuring the accuracy of many topographical and technical details, and also to Paul Latcham for his wise guidance in explaining to me some of the mysteries of book production. To all these and many others I am especially grateful.

Photographs are by the author, unless otherwise credited.

The maps were drawn by David Edwards Associates, Hereford.

A NOTE FROM THE AUTHOR

After a career mostly spent abroad, I retired to this country intending to become better acquainted with my native land. Finding the Home Counties, where I had spent my youth, now clogged with traffic, my wife and I made our way to the Marches where I set eyes on the River Wye for the first time. I knew of its reputation as a beautiful river - after all, it was the lower Wye Valley which gave rise to the cult of the Picturesque; and I knew that it was famous for its salmon, a fish of which I am particularly fond (though I am no fisherman, not having the necessary patience); and I had read that its source was on Plynlimon (Pumlumon Fawr), a few miles from that of the Severn, and that it returned to the same river 150 miles farther on after they had followed widely divergent courses. So now was my chance to discover the Wye for myself.

The map showed that there were many public footpaths in the valley, including the long distance Wye Valley Walk between Chepstow and Rhayader. Because I could find little suitable public transport, it was usually necessary for me to take a circular route, and in order to keep to the valley I tried to make an outward journey on one side of the river and return on the other. This meant bridges, and I gradually became aware of the large number of bridges on the river and their different types. It was during a walk from Chepstow to Monmouth, and while I was eating my sandwiches sitting on a stile facing Bigsweir Bridge, that I really 'saw' the bridge for the first time. It is well known to all motorists who travel along the lower Wye Valley as it is the only bridge on the road between the two towns, and the crossing is controlled by traffic lights. But travelling down the gorge of the lower Wye Valley allows the driver little time to take in the surroundings because of the narrow, and in places tortuous, nature of the road. Now for the first time, I was struck by the slender beauty of this early 19th century cast-iron bridge (**Bigsweir (69)**), and the idea came to me that it would be an agreeable pastime to try to visit all the bridges along the river and to photograph them. (I had no idea then how many of them there were.) When I was a boy at school I collected cigarette cards; later, at university, it was beer mats; now in my second childhood it would be Wye bridges. So that is how the present work was conceived.

Alan Crow
Hereford 1995

INTRODUCTION

THE AIM OF THE STUDY was to identify all the bridge sites, present and past, and to photograph them as a record of the present. This has been supplemented where possible by pictures and descriptions of past bridges. It has not always been possible to find suitable illustrations of earlier bridges and the author is aware that there may be some old bridge sites which he has not recognised. There are seventy-seven bridge sites described, and they are numbered consecutively from source to mouth and arranged numerically each in a separate section of the book with its illustrations. Since the course of the Wye changes direction so frequently it seemed preferable not to use points of the compass in bridge descriptions, but to refer to 'upstream' and 'downstream' and 'left bank' and 'right bank' (looking downstream). This means that the reader's attention is focused on the bridge and the river rather than on the surrounding geography, though compass directions are used when appropriate.

Most of the bridges on the Wye are public roads or rights of way and usually access to them is no problem. Fortunately many rights of way follow the banks more or less closely and it is often possible to walk by the river bank from one bridge to the next - one of the joys of the Wye Valley. The Ordnance Survey maps show the existence of rights of way, and the visitor is urged to keep to them at all times. However, there are many paths which, although not designated as rights of way, are used by the local people and anglers. Visitors using them should remember that they may be technically trespassing and should leave if requested to do so. Several bridges are in fact private but the owners have no objection to their use by *bona fide* members of the public; but there are a few which are on strictly private property, and should not be visited without prior permission. Means of access are indicated in the respective sections where appropriate. Despite every effort to ensure the accuracy of access information the author is unable to guarantee its reliability nor take responsibility for any changes that may have occurred.

Five location maps with an index map are included at the end of the book, but the reader is advised to use a more detailed map when visiting a bridge. Under the heading of each bridge section is a row of figures which refer to the maps. These are: (1) The location map at the end of the book, (2) and (3) the respective sheet numbers of the relevant Ordnance Survey Landranger (1:50 000) and Pathfinder (1:25 000) maps, and (4) the National Grid reference number of the bridge. There is no regular Pathfinder map for much of the lower Wye Valley (Grid square SO 50), and for this stretch of the river, from bridges **68** to **72**, the Ordnance Survey Outdoor Leisure Map, Sheet 14 Wye Valley and

Forest of Dean, which is on the same scale, should be used.

It might help the reader if a brief description in simple terms is given of the different types of bridge construction, with examples to be seen in the Wye Valley. Essentially, there are three types of bridge: **Beam, Arch** and **Suspension**; and all three types have been in use since earliest times. A beam is a horizontal member which is able to resist a load placed on it with a minimum of bending but without breaking. A tree trunk fallen across a stream is an example of a natural beam, and simple wooden beam bridges made of planks thrown across a brook are commonplace. Stone and plain concrete do not usually make good beams, except for very short ones, as they are too brittle, and the ancient clapper bridges made from slabs of granite or other flaggy stones have spans of only a few feet. Where a river is too wide for a single beam, piers of stone or wood are built and the beams placed on them end to end. If necessary, stone piers can be protected from abrasion by floating debris with a row of vertical wooden posts known as starlings. **Nanty footbridge (4)**, near an old lead mine upstream from Llangurig, is a modern example built in 1992 with two concrete cylindrical piers; and farther upstream at **Pont Cefn-brwyn (2)** a wooden beam bridge was built in about 1910 to serve the old Nant Iago lead mines, but later when the wood showed signs of rotting it was strengthened with steel beams and a concrete roadway. The most interesting beam bridge is at **Whitney (40)** where the old toll bridge has three centre spans of wood beams supported on wooden piers and with wood bracing. Dating originally from about 1802 the woodwork has been rebuilt many times.

When the use of iron and steel was developed for industrial use in the late 18th and 19th centuries, simple beams as long and as strong as wood could not be made. Cast iron, like stone, is brittle and was best used for piers and arches, but wrought iron, which is purer, can be forged into bars and angle or channel irons; and these could be connected together by bolting or riveting to make a framework based on the triangle for rigidity. Two longer stringers or chords, one above the other, are connected with a pattern of diagonal and vertical components making a truss girder. Two truss girders are connected with cross beams or transoms and the roadway or deck laid on the transoms. If the truss is predominantly of diagonals criss-crossing one another, it is a lattice girder, and if of panels of sheet iron or steel, it is a plate girder. If the transoms and decks are supported by the lower chords, it is a through bridge, and if by the top chords it is a deck bridge. The truss-girder bridge was a product of the railway age, but many still survive and are a common sight.

An excellent example of a truss-girder through bridge, still standing though no longer a railway bridge, is **Monmouth, Troy (RMR) (66)**. Built in 1874, it has three spans, the two outer ones with parallel chords, but the central one, longer than the others, has an arched top chord which gives it greater strength. **Brockweir Road Bridge (70)** (1828), upstream from Chepstow, is a lattice-girder through bridge and **Lydbrook Junction (62)** (1873), between Ross-on-Wye and Monmouth, is a plate-girder deck bridge, formerly a railway bridge but now used by walkers. Brunel, the celebrated engineer of the Great Western Railway, was an advocate of wooden bridges to save money during the early years of a railway's life, and until it could afford more permanent iron trusses. The four Wye bridges of the Hereford, Ross and Gloucester Railway, **Hereford, Eign (50)**, **Ballingham (52)**, **Strangford (55)**, and **Backney (57)** (see illustration), were all originally built of wood, and were of typical Brunel design. The components of older truss bridges were bars and angle irons, but some modern bridges are different. The footbridge in **Waun Capel Parc (17)** (1965) in Rhayader has tubular components of circular cross-section welded together, and at **Huntsham Bridge (63)** (1982) they are of rectangular cross-section. Another feature of this bridge is that the truss girders are continuous. Although there are two piers and three openings, the girders are welded together as a continuous structure from bank to bank.

A special kind of truss bridge is the Bailey bridge, developed before the Second World War. It comprised a set of components which could be manhandled and readily assembled under battlefield conditions. The truss girder or panel is only 10ft (3.0m) long but the components can be put together in a variety of lengths, widths and load capacities according to the local requirement. The bridge is still manufactured especially for temporary - or in some cases not so temporary - civilian use. There is only one such bridge on the Wye today; it is on the public road leading to the farm at **Ty-mawr (5)**. There was formerly another at nearby **Glangwy (6)**, but it was replaced in 1980 by a concrete beam bridge.

The later development of the rolled-steel joist or I-beam has led to the abandonment of the truss and a return to the simple beam. So too with the prestressed concrete beams in which concrete is poured round stretched high-tensile steel rods which gives concrete a strength comparable to that of steel. Pre-cast beams can be brought to the site in the same way as timber and steel ones and there are many examples on the river of bridges constructed with PSC or RSJ beams. Examples of prestressed concrete beams are at **Llangurig (7)** (1971) and **Hay-on-Wye (38)** (1957), and of rolled-steel joists there is a small footbridge at **Marteg (12)** (1979) and a modern road bridge at **Hoarwithy (53)** (1990).

The **Arch** was a means of bridging a gap with stone, otherwise unsuitable for using as a beam. The principle is to dress the stone into wedge-shaped pieces or vousoirs which when stacked fall naturally into a semicircle, and if accurately faced need no cement to hold them in place. The load on the arch keeps the vousoirs in place as, being semicircular, the weight is transferred vertically to the ground, though in practice, of course, they are cemented to each other to make sure. The problem with the arch is that the roadway or deck must rest on the top of the arch which may necessitate a hump or an embankment; and the triangular spaces between the deck and each side of the arch, the spandrels, need to be filled to support the roadway. Usually this is rubble faced with masonry or brick. Also, with a semicircular arch, the width of the opening is never more than twice the height, which means that many arches are needed to cross a wide river. The Wye's venerable bridges, **Hereford (47)** (1490), **Wilton (59)** (*c*1600) near Ross, and **Monmouth (65)** (1615), are all multi-spanned masonry bridges, and **Bredwardine (41)** (1769), between Hereford and Hay, is built of brick. All these bridges have been strengthened or even rebuilt at some time and cunningly conceal reinforced concrete within their antique faces. **Kerne Road Bridge (60)** (1828) has five graduated arches which give it a particularly elegant appearance. The medieval architects, aiming to produce arches of differing widths but of the same height, in order to join the arcades of naves, aisles and transepts, for example, developed the pointed arch. Bridges rarely need such an arch, unless for decorative effect, but surprisingly there are two at Hereford both at the left bank end: that nearest the bank is a four-centred Tudor arch - it was rebuilt in the late 15th century. Usually bridge builders seek to construct wider arches. This can be achieved with the segmental arch which has a circular arc with a larger radius but not a complete semicircle, and so can be made wider for the same height. This means that the thrust at the springing of the arch is sideways rather than vertical which must be allowed for in the design of piers and abutments. A good example is **Boughrood Road Bridge (35)** built in the 1830s. Another is **Monmouth Wye Bridge (65)** where the original semicircular arches are partly hidden by the later segmental ones added when the bridge was widened in 1879. A similar result is obtained from a three-centred arch which springs vertically from the pier with a relatively narrow arc, but the curve is flatter over the greater part of the arch. Such an arch can be seen in the six-span bridge at **Builth Wells (32)** (1779, widened in 1924).

Arched bridges have also been made of cast or wrought-iron segments, bolted or riveted together. In these cases the spandrels are open, and the deck and the arch are braced together, sometimes with decorative facing. **Chepstow Old Bridge (74)** (1816) is an elegant example in cast iron, and **Hunderton Bridge (45)** (1912) is another of wrought-iron plates riveted together. The

French introduced reinforced concrete into Britain in about 1900. The insertion of iron rods and mesh before the concrete is poured gives it greater strength enabling it to be used for arches instead of just for decking. Both elements can be poured as a whole and the distinction between arch and beam becomes blurred and an arched beam is created. The road bridge at **Newbridge-on-Wye (29)** (1911) was the first reinforced-concrete bridge to be built on the Wye. It had slender segmental arches but had to be demolished in 1978 and was replaced by a simple beam bridge, but also of reinforced concrete. The introduction of prestressed concrete enabled arched beams to be built of even more slender proportions. **Greyfriars Bridge (46)** in Hereford, built in 1966, is a single span example, but the appearance of brick-filled spandrels is an illusion as this is a decorative facade. Even more graceful is **Bridstow Bridge (58)** (1960) which carries the A40 over the river near Ross-on-Wye. This is an example of a cantilever bridge. The two main spans are balanced on the piers near the centre of the span instead of being supported at each end, and are joined at the centre of the bridge by a short suspended span which rests on the ends of the main spans. (The join cannot easily be detected from a distance.) The ends of the main spans are anchored down on the abutments to prevent them lifting when the other end is under load.

An unusual bridge has recently made its appearance on the Wye. It is a wooden arched footbridge at **Cwmbach (15)** upstream from Rhayader and was built in 1994. The arch is constructed from laminated softwood planks bent into shape and glued together. The deck is also of wood and supported by wooden bracing in the spandrels, and the arch is hinged at the crest as well as on each side to accommodate the greater flexibility of wood.

The third type of construction is the **Suspension** bridge. In its most primitive form it consists of three ropes slung across the river, a lower one to walk on, and two higher ones to grasp with the hands. A more advanced type would have two lower ropes to support a wooden footway. The Forest Enterprise bridge at **Biblins (64)** in the Forest of Dean, built in 1957, is essentially of this type. Four steel cables are slung between wooden towers and anchored to the ground at either end and the user has to climb a stairway to reach the deck. Because all the cables follow a natural catenary curve there is a strong tendency to sway from side to side, and to prevent this, sway cables connect the deck with the river bank at a distance from the bridge. In the more usual type of bridge, the deck is suspended from the catenary by suspenders the lengths of which vary to allow the deck to be more horizontal or even slightly arched. The deck is usually stiffened with truss girders or with lighter cables tensioned and anchored at each end. In order to allow controlled movement in such a flexible structure, the cables are either carried over the tops of the towers on rollers or, if anchored to the top, the towers are hinged at the bottom. Examples of all kinds can be seen on the Wye. The oldest suspension bridge on the river is the private bridge at **Ystrad (26)** on the Doldowlod estate near Llanwrthwl. It is a stock bridge built in about 1880. The catenaries are chains constructed from parallel eye-ended rods connected end-to-end with bolts. **Llanstephan (34)** (1922) is a road bridge with twin steel cables and stiffened with lattice girders. (At the time of writing it is closed to traffic pending the replacement of the cables which had become dangerously corroded.) **Victoria Bridge (48)**, one of the attractions of Hereford and built to commemorate Queen Victoria's Diamond Jubilee, is a classic example with bar chains and stiffened with lattice girders and with hinged towers. **Sellack (54)** (1895) and **Foy (56)** (1921), upstream from Ross, are neighbours. Both are country parish footbridges, the former with closely spaced suspenders and stiffened with cables along the decks, and the latter stiffened with truss girders. There are two unusual suspension footbridges at **Dernol (9)** (*c*1975) and **Cwmcoch (14)** (1962) both between Llangurig and Rhayader and almost identical. The main cables directly support the central section of the deck though they are not anchored to it. There are no suspenders but additional support for the deck is obtained from six slender cables tightly tensioned to minimise sag. The lack of effective stiffening allows the bridge to sway, and they are locally known as 'swing' bridges.

The **Wye Section (77)** of the Severn Bridge, which carries the M4 motorway between England and Wales, was opened in 1966 and strengthened in 1982. It is often regarded as a suspension bridge though it is very different from its neighbour across the Severn itself. It is called a cable-stayed bridge and is in effect a cantilevered beam bridge. The cables are anchored to the towers as well as to the deck, and so create a near-rigid triangle; and a similar arrangement exists on the bank side of each tower, so that the two sides are balanced. The two towers are single posts set on the centre line of the bridge, and there are no suspenders. This bridge is a striking example of modern bridge building.

A fourth type of bridge is the movable bridge, generally associated with shipping lanes to allow the passage of tall vessels. Although no such bridge exists on the Wye today, the predecessor of **Biblins (64)** was a transporter bridge in which a cradle with pulleys was suspended from a cable and dragged back and forth carrying logs and workers across the river (see illustration). It stopped working in about 1929.

THE BRIDGES

1 Y DRUM   Private farm track

Map 1; 136; 928; SN 854 828

THE FIRST BRIDGE across the River Wye is situated 3.2km below its source high on the south-eastern slope of Plynlimon. It carries a track which branches off from the main farm road following the valley of the young river upstream 3km from **Pont Rhydgaled (3)** and is named after a nearby hill. The bridge is a steel beam structure with wooden deck, its single span 10m long and 2.5m wide and supported in midstream by two cylindrical columns. It was built by the owner of Pont Rhydgaled sheep farm in about 1965 to give access for his farm vehicles to the grazing lands below Plynlimon in addition to an existing ford for heavier lorries. The location of the bridge is at the site of a disused lead mine, known variously as New Van or West Wye Valley, which ceased production in the mid 1880s, and some of the old mine buildings have been adapted for farm use. In the photograph the view is upstream towards its source 3km away, but hidden behind the trees.

The farm road from Pont Rhydgaled leading northward off the A44 highway is a public right of way but there is no access for motor vehicles without permission from the farm. There is no public right of way from Y Drum to the source on Plynlimon, but the farm road, still a right of way, continues for a further 3.5km through Hafren Forest to reach the River Severn (Afon Hafren). (DB, HJH, SBE)

Y DRUM   Looking upstream; the peaks of Plynlimon (Pumlumon) are hidden behind the trees 3km away.

2 PONT CEFN-BRWYN   Private farm road from Pont Rhydgaled on the A44

Map 1; 136; 928; SN 830 836

THE BRIDGE is 1.6km downstream from **Y Drum** bridge (**1**) and 1.2km along the farm road from Pont Rhydgaled. This road continues north past Y Drum, and then follows the valley of Nant Iago, a tributary of the Wye, to Hafren Forest. The bridge was built in about 1910 to serve a lead mine at the head of Nant Iago, and consisted of two spans each of four massive pinewood beams supported on a stone pier. The mine was opened in about 1846 and always had a struggle to keep going, but it enjoyed a brief period of activity during the First World War. The workings were primitive and the owner was unable to meet the cost of maintaining legal safety requirements, and the mine was closed probably soon after the end of the war. Ironically, it was the only mine of several in the upper Wye Valley which lasted into the twentieth century.

In about 1975 the bridge was strengthened for the Institute of Hydrology to enable their vehicles to reach the weir which was being built a few metres upstream. Steel joists were added which supported a base of corrugated iron on to which a reinforced concrete deck was poured. The original timber beams were left in place but they no longer support the load. As can be seen from the photograph, one of the original beams is now rotted and falling apart.

The farm road leaving the A44 at Pont Rhydgaled is a public right of way, but not for vehicles, for which permission should be obtained from the farm. (DB, SBE)

PONT CEFN-BRWYN   The original wooden beams are falling away leaving steel joists to carry the weight of the farm traffic.

3 PONT RHYDGALED   A44 between Llangurig and Aberystwyth

Map 1; 136; 928; SN 841 827

THIS BRIDGE carries trunk road traffic from the midlands and the south, which converges on Llangurig and continues on to Aberystwyth. It was built in 1800, a simple segmental-arched structure of masonry, presumably to replace a ford (the meaning of 'rhyd'). At that time, there was no road between Rhayader and Llangurig and traffic from the south to Aberystwyth took the road through Devil's Bridge or went a long way round through Newtown. But in 1830 the road from Rhayader to Llangurig was opened - the New Aberystwyth Coach Road - and the increased traffic necessitated its widening which took place in 1840.

In 1980, the bridge was widened again and the old arch was almost obscured by superimposing prestressed concrete beams and deck. Whereas the old arch was built square to the river, the present structure runs skew, following the general alignment of the road. The bridge is located just above the confluence of the Tarrenig with the Wye, and the A44, after crossing the bridge, leaves the Wye valley and follows a more westerly route up the Tarrenig valley towards Aberystwyth.

Car travellers speeding their way to Aberystwyth may hardly be aware that they are crossing a bridge or that it is over the Wye, but the venerable arch can be viewed, still in place under its concrete cover, by clambering down either bank of the downstream side of the bridge. The junction of the two rivers can be seen from a steel and concrete bridge which takes a Forest Enterprise road from the nearby car park across the Tarrenig.

(BLc, HW, KK2, PHD)

PONT RHYDGALED   The earlier masonry arch can be seen underneath the later prestressed concrete addition which is on the skew.

The bridge as it appeared after its widening in 1840.   *Hereford and Worcester County Libraries*

4 NANTY   Footpath from the A44 to Nanty farm and beyond

Map 1; 136; 928; SN 854 820

THIS SPLENDIDLY ROBUST 3-span wooden footbridge is, at the time of writing, the second youngest bridge on the River Wye. (The youngest is **Cwmbach (19)** built in 1994.) It was built in 1992 to replace an earlier one which had been repaired in 1989, but which had become unsafe. It is situated at a point where the river and the A44 from Llangurig to Aberystwyth following the left bank are close together. It carries a public right of way across the valley to Nanty Farm and thence through the Forest Enterprise forest to the headwaters of Afon Ystwyth, a distance of 8km. The bridge is on the site of the old Nanty lead mine which closed in 1867, and is sometimes known as Nanty Mine bridge. The mine followed a lode which struck north from river level, passed under the road, and continued up the hill on the other side known as Allt Pant-mawr. (The mine was also known as Pantmawr Mine.) The course of the lode can be followed today from the spoil heaps left from the successive adit levels driven into the hillside.

   The photograph shows the substantial nature of the cylindrical concrete piers designed to withstand the onslaught of torrents in time of flood. The view is from the left bank, and the bare hill in the distance is called Llechwedd Llwyd which means 'grey hillside'.

(DB, PHD)

NANTY   A simple wood beam footbridge built in 1992, viewed from the left bank.

5 TY-MAWR   Bailey bridge, minor road between A44 and Ty-mawr farm

Map 1; 136; 928; SN 873 808

THIS BRIDGE DESIGN is named after its inventor Sir Donald Bailey (1901-1985) who, before the Second World War, conceived the idea of a prefabricated bridge-building kit using standard components which could be easily transported and assembled under the adverse conditions of war. Furthermore they could be used variously according to the size and strength of the bridge required.

The basic component was a rectangular steel truss or 'panel' measuring 10ft by 5ft with a vertical brace in the centre and diagonals on either side. The top and bottom chords were drilled with a horizontal hole at one end and fitted with a projecting lug with a similar hole at the other, so that the panels could be bolted together end to end according to the length of span needed. The assembled panels were connected cross-wise with joists clamped on to the bottom chords, and on these rested steel stringers and a timber deck. For greater strength the panels could be sandwiched side by side in doublets or triplets, or even on top of each other, and there were other components for walkways, ramps, etc. After the war many of the bridges were reused for civilian purposes, and new ones are still being manufactured, though with various modifications.

The bridge at Ty-mawr was erected after the great flood of 1960-61 had washed away a footbridge. (At that time vehicles crossed the river by a ford.) It is 18.3m (60ft) long, i.e. six panels, and 4.3m (14ft) wide. The bridge is rusting and gives an impression of age, but no record of its origin has been found. However, it has been identified as of 1940 vintage and probably of ex-Army origin, but there are some non-standard features which suggest a composite assemblage. No doubt its components have been used previously elsewhere, perhaps many times.

The bridge is public, maintained by Powys County Council, and there are several rights of way leading from the bridge on both sides of the river but they are not at present signed. The footings for the old footbridge can still be seen alongside the bridge upstream. and the ford can be identified a little way below the bridge.

Ty-mawr is the only Bailey bridge on the Wye, though there was one at **Glangwy (6)**, since replaced in 1980. There is also one across the River Elan, below the dams and leading to Elan village, in which the panels on the upstream side are assembled in doublets.
(IWM, PT, RMRE)

TY-MAWR   A Bailey bridge designed for military use and including components dating from the 1940s.
The view is from Ty-Mawr farm on the right bank looking north.

6 GLANGWY   Minor road connecting the A44 with the Ystwyth Valley

Map 1; 136; 928; SN 893 801

THIS IS A SINGLE SPAN prestressed-concrete beam bridge with a slab deck, just about the simplest possible type of modern concrete construction. It is 22.6m long and 5.5m wide, and was built by Mabey in 1980 to replace a Bailey bridge which had become unsafe. The latter had probably been built after the great flood of 1960-61 like its neighbour upstream at **Ty-mawr (5)**, but nine panels long instead of six. The lower photograph shows that the bridge was supported in midstream by a pier of twin iron columns with diagonal bracing. Normally, Bailey bridges of spans up to 73m long could be assembled without piers, but to ensure speedy bolting a greater tolerance than normal was used for the connecting bolt holes. This gave longer spans a distinct but acceptable sag. Perhaps, with the use of worn secondhand components, it was thought prudent to add a pier, though the bridge at Ty-mawr was erected without one. After demolishing the bridge, Mabey were able to reconstruct six-panel units for use as a temporary structure alongside, while the new bridge was under construction on the site of the old one. The abutments for this bridge can still be seen.

There are rights of way along the left bank upstream to the main road, and along the right bank downstream for a short distance. But the road over the bridge leads for 9km across remote country along the south-eastern flank of the Esgair Ychion group of hills, and is joined by two branches of a footpath through the Forest Enterprise forest from **Nanty (4)** before it descends into the valley of Afon Ystwyth. Here it joins the old coach road from Rhayader to Aberystwyth (see **Rhayader (18)**) 1.5km or so above the abandoned Cwmystwyth lead mines.

(PCA, PHD)

GLANGWY   A prestressed-concrete beam bridge built in 1980 looking upstream. The abandoned abutments of its predecessor can be seen.

A Bailey bridge probably built in the early 1960s and replaced by the present bridge.

Powys County Archives Office

7 LLANGURIG   Minor road from Llangurig leading downstream along the right bank

Map 1; 136/147; 948; SN 908 796

LLANGURIG IS THE FIRST TOWN on the River Wye in its descent from Plynlimon (Pumlumon Fawr). It lies on the road from Newtown and Llanidloes westward to Aberystwyth before it crosses the river at **Pont Rhydgaled (3)**, 7km higher up. For many years Pont Llangurig was an important crossing of the Wye, as until the turnpike between Rhayader and Llangurig (now the A470) was opened along the left bank in 1830, the only road between these towns was along the right bank, though it was not suitable for coaches. The bridge is located at a pool which is said to be the highest point reached by the salmon when they come up the river to spawn.

The present bridge was opened in 1971. It is a stark single-span composite structure of prestressed-concrete beams and concrete deck supported on masonry abutments and is 22m long and 6.4m wide. It replaced a 3-span bridge constructed from fabricated iron beams, supported on masonry abutments (which were rebuilt for the present bridge) and on two piers each of three rather slender iron columns, apparently without bracing. The bridge was damaged beyond repair in the great flood of winter 1965-66 when, according to local townsfolk, blocks of ice 'as big as motor cars' crashed into the piers, destroying them and allowing the beams to buckle under their own weight.

There is a record of a bridge at Llangurig, almost certainly of stone, in the early eighteenth century which was repaired in 1713 at a cost of £20.

There are no rights of way along the river banks here, although there is a farm road leading upstream for a short distance along the right bank from which the bridge can be viewed, and the town car park is close to the bridge of the left bank. The bridge itself is public, of course, and the road follows the right bank of the river down to the next bridge, **Pant-y-Drain (8)**, a distance of 3.2km, and thence to those at **Dernol (9)**, **Rhyd Dol Llech (10)**, **Cwmcoch (14)**, and **Cwmbach (15)**, all of which cross the river to connect with the A470 along the left bank, and eventually reaching Rhayader after 16km.

(BLc, EJ, JAC, PHD)

LLANGURIG   A concrete beam bridge built in 1971 to replace the iron one below, looking upstream.

The earlier iron bridge which was damaged by flood in 1966, looking downstream.   *Monmouth Museum*

8 PANT-Y-DRAIN   Private road connecting Pant-y-Drain farmhouse on the minor road along the right bank with the A470 along the left bank

Map 1; 136/147; 948; SN 916 763

THIS PRIVATE FARM ROAD BRIDGE is said to have been built in the late 1960s replacing a footbridge and a ford, the latter of which is still usable. Doubtless, its construction was a consequence of the flood of 1965-66 which severely damaged the bridge at **Llangurig (7)**, 3km upstream. The bridge is built of steel joists in two spans supported on concrete abutments and a concrete slab pier. The deck and the railings were replaced about ten years ago. The photograph is taken from the right bank. The ford is on the downstream side of the bridge and its approach road from the A470 can be seen passing under the far span.

   Although this is a private bridge, the present owner of the property allows the public to use it at its own risk.

(DV)

PANT-Y-DRAIN   A private farm bridge built in the late 1960s to replace a footbridge and a ford. The latter can still be seen.

9 DERNOL   Public footpath connecting Dernol on the right bank with A470 along the left bank

Map 1; 136/147; 948; SN 917 749

BUILT BY N.R. HOPE of Newbridge-on-Wye in about 1975, Dernol is one of several light suspension bridges of a distinctive design which at one time or another have been built across the upper reaches of the River. This one has two main cables, 25mm diameter, which run over steel rollers at the top of the towers, and are anchored at each end to stout oak stanchions. There are no suspenders, but a short length of the deck midway along the span is supported directly on both sides by the main cables. These pass freely through grooves along the underside of wooden bars which are attached to the deck structure, and which, like the rollers at the top of the towers, allow for some movement in the structure when under load. The deck consists of transverse wooden cradles 0.6m apart resting on six slender parallel cables which, like the main cables, are tensioned and anchored to the stanchions at either end of the bridge. In addition, every third cradle carries a strongly braced vertical post at each end, and these also are supported on horizontal tensioned cables, two on each side. Although these posts and cables serve the purpose of protective railings, they are in fact an integral part of the whole load-bearing structure. The walkway over the cradles consists of wooden planks. The towers, made of larch wood, are 16.8m apart and the total length of the bridge is about 24m and the width 0.8m. The fact that the whole structure, including the deck, depends on a system of cables - two over the towers and ten along the deck - inevitably gives it considerable flexibility, and bridges of this type are known locally as 'swing' bridges - not of course to be confused with the movable bridges to be found crossing ship canals.

The footpath from Dernol on the right bank is a right of way, and after crossing the bridge it splits into two, one striking north-east to Neuadd-ddu on the A470, and the other south-east to join the same road farther south.

Other 'swing' bridges on the Wye which are still in use are at **Cwmcoch (14)** and a private bridge at **Glaslyn (22)**; and another, only recently replaced by a timber arch, was at **Cwmbach (15)**. Two others on the private estate at **Doldowlod (25)** and **(27)**, and a third, **Felindre (19)** at Rhayader, have almost completely disappeared.

(NRH)

DERNOL   A 'swing' suspension footbridge seen from the right bank.

10 RHYD DOL LLECH   Connecting the minor road from Llangurig along the right bank with A447 along left bank

Map 1; 136/147; 948; SN 921 738

THE OFFICIAL NAME of this bridge means 'the ford by the meadow of slates', indicating that the crossing was once a ford; but the name does not appear on the Ordnance Survey map, and it is more easily identified with Tynant, a nearby farmhouse.

The present bridge, the second at this location, was built in 1978, and is a 2-span composite structure of prestressed-concrete inverted T-beams with a concrete deck. The abutments and the central pier are of reinforced concrete and the total length of the bridge is 28.6m and the width 5.9m.

The first bridge, which replaced the ford, was an all-steel structure of two spans with longitudinal and transverse beams, as well as the deck plates, of the same material. The abutments and the pier were of brick. Early in 1975, an inspection of the bridge showed that the beams were badly corroded and were twisted and sagging. Early demolition was considered necessary and a weight restriction order was placed on it later in the year.

The bridge can be reached from either of the roads following the river banks; there are no additional rights of way.

(PCA, PHD)

RHYD DOL LLECH   A prestressed-concrete bridge built in 1978, looking downstream.

11 GLYN GWY   Private footbridge

AS ITS NAME IMPLIES, this bridge is situated in a narrow rocky glen of the Wye, thickly wooded and extending for about 1.5km above its confluence with the River Marteg. It is a delightful little bridge in private residential grounds on the left bank of the river and consists of a simple arched slab of reinforced concrete with the railing posts incorporated in the concrete. No record has been traced of its origin, but it is believed to have been built in the 1920s, and would seem to be an unusual design for a bridge of this construction at that date. The earliest reinforced-concrete bridge on the Wye was built in 1911 at **Newbridge-on-Wye (29)**, but it was demolished about 1979. The consulting engineers for that bridge were L.G. Mouchel who introduced the technique of reinforced concrete into Britain from France; but it is not known whether this firm was involved in building Glyn Gwy bridge. It was probably built, like several other bridges over the river, to enable the owner to fish from the other side. In those days the land on the right bank formed part of the Vaughan Prickard family's Dderw estate which extended downstream to beyond Rhayader, but it has since changed hands.

As can be seen from the photograph, the arch springs directly from a natural rocky foundation, and the bridge has evidently withstood the torrents of previous years which have destroyed so many other bridges on the river. There is no public access to the bridge from either bank.
(BLc, BWM)

GLYN GWY   An arched slab bridge of reinforced concrete linking private estates on either side of the river, probably built in the 1920s.

12 MARTEG   Footpath from A470 to the right bank

Map 1; 136/147; 948; SN 951 715

OWNED BY the Rhayader Angling Society, this is a steel I-beam bridge on masonry abutments and a single pier on the left bank, with a length of 21m and a width of 0.7m. It is set in a narrow secluded wooded stretch of the river just above its confluence with the River Marteg, and was built in 1979 by Bernard Lloyd of Rhayader to replace a simple wooden beam bridge which had become dangerous with age. This earlier one had been provided by Alderman Vaughan Prickard to enable the tenants of his Dderw estate on the right bank to reach the main road into Rhayader. The angling society holds the fishing rights on the estate downstream as far as Rhayader, and they built the present bridge at their own expense.

A right of way leads upstream from the road, but it crosses the river by a ford a few yards upstream from the bridge which is technically private, though the present owners allow the public to use it without hindrance. The right of way follows the rocky bank upstream for about 750m, eventually climbing the valley side to reach the minor road between Rhayader and Llangurig. There is a roadside car park by the A470 close to the bridge and a few yards north of the junction with the minor road to St Harmon. This is named on the map as Pont Marteg which refers to the road bridge across that river.

(BLd, GHR)

MARTEG   The present steel beam bridge built in 1979, looking upstream.

The earlier wooden bridge.   *Monmouth Museum*

13 CWMCOCH, rail   Dismantled, former Mid-Wales Railway

Map 1; 136/147; 948; SN 947 706

THE MID-WALES RAILWAY was opened in 1864 between Llanidloes, on the Llanidloes and Newtown Railway, and Three Cocks, near Glasbury, on the Hereford and Brecon Railway, though it had running powers between Moat Lane Junction on the Newtown and Machynlleth Railway and Brecon. The line descended into the Wye Valley through the Marteg Valley and left it at Three Cocks, a distance of 19km in which it crossed the Wye five times as well as a major bridge across the Ithon, just above its confluence with the Wye. The five bridges were at **Cwmcoch (13)**, **Glyn (21)**, **Nant-y-Craig (24)**, **Newbridge-on-Wye (28)** and **Boughrood (36)**. Of these only that at Glyn is still standing. T.R. Perkins, writing in 1938, reported that between Cwmcoch and Three Cocks there were a number of plate-girder bridges, though Boughrood was certainly of lattice-girder construction. These girders were probably not the original ones of 1864 which, when built, were probably of lattice-girder construction and supported on piers of cast-iron piping grouped into three, identical with those at **Brynwern Bridge (30)**. There can be little doubt that, as at Brynwern, they were fabricated by the W. Thomas Railway Works at Llanidloes, and since it is known that the prolific S.W. Williams of Rhayader worked on the Cambrian Railways, he may well have been involved in this and the other bridges of the Mid-Wales Railway. Later, in the 1920s, the piers were encased in concrete in the form of arched portals, giving greater strength for the heavier locomotives then in use, and it is possible that stronger girders were installed at the same time (see Boughrood). Cwmcoch bridge had three spans and (except for the Ithon bridge) is the only one where the piers are still in place.

In 1888 the working of the Mid-Wales Railway was taken over by the Cambrian Railways, by then owner of most of the North Wales rail network, but legally the Mid-Wales remained independent until it was finally amalgamated with the Cambrian in 1904. In the grouping of 1922 the Cambrian became part of the Great Western Railway until nationalisation in 1948. Proposals to close the line were announced in 1962 and the last train to run was on 31 December of that year. The track and the bridges were dismantled not long after.

The piers can be seen close to the minor road which passes Cwmcoch farm on the right bank of the river, and the path which crosses the river by **Cwmcoch footbridge (14)** also passes through a cutting in the embankment leading to the south abutment.

(JBG2, RCRM, RWK, TRP)

CWMCOCH, rail   The original cast-iron piers were encased in concrete, looking upstream.

14 CWMCOCH, footbridge   Farm track connecting the A470 along the left bank with a minor road along the right bank

Map 1; 136/147; 948; SN 948 705

THE BRIDGE IS SITUATED 200m downstream from the dismantled **Cwmcoch railway bridge (13)**. It is a 'swing' bridge built in 1967 by N.R. Hope of Newbridge-on-Wye, and is of almost identical construction to that at **Dernol (9)**. It is however much longer. The distance between towers is about 24m and, with long approach ramps, the total length is about 53m and its width 0.8m, as at Dernol - a splendid example of this kind of suspension bridge.

It replaced a wooden beam bridge of three spans and two timber piers which was washed away in the great flood of 1960. This bridge was 1m wide and had massive masonry abutments which were used as foundations for the towers of the present bridge. It was built alongside a ford and was used for driving sheep as well as for pedestrians. After it was destroyed, it was considered that the opportunity should be taken to replace it with a vehicular bridge or at least one capable of carrying a tractor, and Radnorshire County Council applied to the Ministry of Agriculture and Fisheries for a grant for this purpose. But the application was turned down on the grounds that the previous bridge was only a stock and pedestrian bridge, and a grant could not be made for more ambitious use. There followed protracted discussions, and in 1963 the situation looked sufficiently encouraging for the Council to obtain a quotations from Messrs Tubewrights Limited, at that time based in Newport, to build a steel vehicular bridge, but a final refusal by the Ministry led to the adoption of the present 'swing' bridge. In 1965, Tubewrights built the replacement for a bridge in Rhayader which was also destroyed in the flood of 1960 (See **Rhayader, Waun Capel Parc(17)**).

Although the bridge is publicly owned, it is not recorded as a right of way. It supplements the ford, which is still usable for vehicles, and connects with a farm track on both sides of the river, and it is used by the local community. Before joining the road on the right bank, the track passes through a gap, formerly under a bridge, in the embankment approach to Cwmcoch railway bridge.

(NRH, PCA)

CWMCOCH, footbridge   A 'swing' suspension footbridge seen from the right bank.

15 CWMBACH   Footpath connecting A470 along left bank with minor road between Rhayader and Llangurig along right bank

Map 1; 136/147; 969; SO 955 698

CWMBACH FOOTBRIDGE (near Rhayader) is the latest bridge to be built on the Wye and its design is quite unique to the river. It was constructed by Tysons plc of Liverpool, and was completed in August 1994. It consists of a segmental-arched beam of laminated wood springing from the vertical faces of concrete abutments. There are actually two beams 84cm x 20cm in cross-section, assembled into a stack of 22 planks 3.8cm thick, bent to the required curvature and glued together. The wooden deck is also arched but of less curvature, springing from the top of the abutments and supported by bracing in the spandrels, and is edged with wooden posts and railings. In fact almost the whole bridge is of wood - locally grown fir for the arches and the rest of oak - held together with glue and wooden dowels, the exception being the massive iron hinges. This too is an unusual feature. Whereas iron and steel arches usually spring from hinges to allow slight flexing of the metal, this bridge is fitted with additional hinges at the crest of the arch to accommodate the greater flexibility of the laminated wood. But it has to be said that the prominent hinge in this position detracts somewhat from the appearance of the arch by breaking the continuity of the curve. Even so, Cwmbach, with its hand-crafted appearance and the warm natural colour of the varnished wood, must be one of the most attractive small bridges on the River Wye.

Its predecessor was a 'swing' bridge like those at **Dernol (9)** and **Cwmcoch (footbridge) (13)** and was built in 1962 to replace an earlier (beam?) bridge destroyed in the flood of 1960. It became unsafe and was demolished in 1991. (CTG, GD, PHD)

CWMBACH   An unusual laminated wooden arched footbridge built in 1994, seen from the left bank.

The earlier 'swing' bridge demolished in 1992.

Powys Highways Department

16 RHAYADER, Gwardolau Site of former private footbridge

Map 1; 136/147; 969; SN 965 687

THE BRIDGE WAS BUILT in 1930 to enable pedestrians to reach the Gwardolau estate on the right bank from the A470, and was sited alongside an existing ford for wheeled traffic and equestrians. Construction was started by the estate staff, but apparently they ran into problems and Morgan Lloyd & Sons, building contractors of Rhayader, were engaged to complete it. The bridge consisted of iron beams in three spans with a wooden deck. The centre span rested at one end on a concrete footing on the left bank, and the other end was supported by an iron pillar embedded in the river. Two approach spans sloped to ground level. In the flood of 1960-61, which also damaged the bridge in **Waun Capel Parc (17)**, a tree demolished the central pillar and the bridge collapsed, but it was not rebuilt.

Although the bridge was privately owned, it was regularly used by the local public, especially anglers, without objection from the owners. The site lies just upstream from the northern end of Rhayader Caravan Park; it can be seen by crossing Waun Capel Parc bridge and following a pleasant woodland walk upstream along the right bank for 700m, but fragments of the footings are all that remain today.

(BLd)

GWARDOLAU   Site of a private footbridge demolished by flood in 1960-61, looking upstream. The Gwardolau estate is on the left.

The bridge, built in 1930, before it was demolished. The figure is standing on the centre span.

Hereford and Worcester County Libraries

17 RHAYADER, Waun Capel Parc   Public amenity footpath

Map 1; 136/147; 969; SN 968 681

THIS DISTINCTIVE SINGLE SPAN FOOTBRIDGE consists of three continuous truss girders constructed from welded steel tubes of circular cross-section. The total length is 30m and width 1.8m . It was erected in 1965 as a training exercise for 101 Squadron (TA) of the Royal Monmouthshire Royal Engineers - a military unit dating back to 1660, and the only one in the army to have two 'Royals' in its title - and opened amid much rejoicing by Mr R.L. Ryder, chairman of the Rhayader Parish Council. The bridge was fabricated by Tubewrights Limited, specialists in tubular steel structures (later absorbed by the British Steel Corporation) at their works in Newport, Monmouthshire, and transported in sections to Rhayader by road. At that time the Newport works was being closed while the firm was transferring its centre to a large new works at Liverpool and the bridge was probably among the last to be built at Newport.

In 1953, Alderman Vaughan Prickard presented to the town a strip of woodland which was part of his Dderw estate bordering the river on the right bank to be added to the recreation park on the opposite side. At the same time he donated sufficient timber from his estate for an ornamental bridge which was built by Bernard Lloyd of Rhayader. However, like so many other bridges on the upper part of the Wye it was a victim of the great flood of December 1960 and had to be abandoned. So the residents of Rhayader had every reason to rejoice now that they could again reach their woodlands on the other side of the river. There is a pleasant walk for about 500m through the woods upstream as far as the site of the old **Gwardolau Bridge (16)**.

(BLd, PW, RMRE)

WAUN CAPEL PARC   Public recreational truss bridge of welded steel tubes erected by the Territorial Army in 1965.

18 RHAYADER, town bridge   B4518 to the Elan
Valley dams

Map 1; 136/147; 969; SN 968 679

WHEN THE WYE REACHES RHAYADER it encounters a rocky channel, and the resulting cataract gave the town its proper name of Rhaeadr Gwy meaning the 'waterfall of the Wye'. The bridge was built across the cataract in 1780, and it is said that the latter was much reduced as a consequence, but the falls below the bridge are still quite impressive, especially when the river is in spate. Most of the town lies on the left bank or east side of the river, but the smaller community on the other side is known as Cwmdeuddwr. Consequently the townsfolk call the bridge Cwmdeuddwr Bridge, because that is where it leads to, whereas their neighbours on the other side - and the rest of the world - know it simply as Rhayader Bridge.

It has a single segmental arch of stone with a span of 18.3m and a width of 8.3m. It was reconstructed in 1929 by Radnorshire County Council and strengthened with concrete. At that time the bridge had a distinct hump, and the crest of the arch was lowered to more truly segmental profile, and the hump reduced. An engraving of the bridge made in about 1820 suggests that at one time the hump was even more pronounced. The illustrations, both looking upstream, show the distinct hump before the reconstruction. The lower photograph also shows the rocks which create such an impressive cascade when the river is in spate.

Originally the bridge was built to carry the coach road to Devil's Bridge and Aberystwyth (the Old Coach Road or Mountain Road as it is known today) but was largely superseded in 1830 when the new turnpike was opened to Aberystwyth through Llangurig (now the A470 and A44). Today the bridge is important as it carries the B4518 to the popular Elan Valley and its reservoirs.

The bridge is best seen from the recreation grounds by the river below the bridge where, when the water is low, the rocks are exposed and can be clambered upon.

(BLc, KK2, EJ, PHD)

TOWN BRIDGE   Masonry arch originally built in 1780, but showing the concrete strengthening added during the rebuilding of 1929.

The bridge before the 1929 reconstruction, showing a more pronounced hump.

Hereford & Worcester County Libraries

19 RHAYADER, Felindre   Site of former private suspension footbridge

Map 1; 136/147; 969; SN 974 676

FELINDRE IS ON THE LEFT BANK of the river at the end of South Street, Rhayader, where the A470 to Builth crosses Rhyd-hir Brook at its confluence with the Wye. The bridge was built to enable the tenants of the Ddole Farm estate to reach Rhayader. The farm buildings lie on the right bank of the river 400m downstream from the bridge, and the associated fields once covered an extensive area on both sides of the river between the farm and the town. The road from Rhayader to the farm led from Cwmdeuddwr, on the far side of the town bridge, and along the slope of a wooded hill. As a result of extensive tree felling on the hill during the First World War, a landslide blocked the road from Cwmdeuddwr for many years. At that time, the farm formed part of the Dderw estate and was owned by Alderman Prickard, and as an alternative he built the bridge at Felindre for his pedestrian tenants, while farm traffic was able to cross the river by a ford a short distance upstream from the bridge. Later, when Alderman Prickard decided to sell Ddole (the land on the left bank became playing fields and a public recreation park), he had the road re-opened and both the bridge and the ford fell into disuse, though the latter is still used by equestrians.

The bridge was a 'swing' bridge (see **Dernol (9)**) suspended from cables taken from the shaft of a South Wales coal mine, having reached their legal age limit. All that remains today are the wooden stanchions which anchored the ends of the cables. There are rights of way along both sides of the river, that on the left bank between Felindre and the sewage works, and that on the right bank from Ddole Farm to the ford just upstream from the bridge site. There is a new housing development along the left bank, but the right of way is still in existence. Both paths pass by **Ddole water pipeline bridge (20)**.
(BLd)

FELINDRE   All that remains of the footbridge linking the former Ddole farm estate on the far side with the road to Rhayader.

20 RHAYADER, Ddole Pipeline bridge carrying water from the Elan Valley to Birmingham

Map 1; 136/147; 969; SN 976 675

BUILT IN 1969, the bridge is a late addition to the aqueduct bringing water to Birmingham from the hills of Mid Wales. It consists of a single 60in (1.52m) diameter steel pipe supported at each end on a bed of masonry. In 1892 an Act of Parliament received the Royal Assent for the City of Birmingham to construct dams across the Elan Valley, and for an aqueduct to carry the impounded water to the city 116 km distant. Three dams were built creating a series of reservoirs, of which the lowest is Caban Coch from which the water is drawn. The point of withdrawal is 51.5m higher in elevation than Birmingham, so the water is able to flow by gravity along a reasonably direct route to its destination. For much of its journey it flows at atmospheric pressure along underground conduits, like canal tunnels, down a gentle gradient of about 1 in 2300; but where the route crosses a valley the water is transferred to inverted siphons, main pipelines which lead down to the bottom of the valley creating a natural head, and so up the other side to join another conduit on a gradient in line with the previous one. About half of the aqueduct consists of underground conduits and half of steel pipeline. When King Edward VII turned on the valves to inaugurate the Elan Aqueduct in 1904, there were two mains each 42in (1.06m) in diameter, and in 1939 a third of 60in was added. Where the mains had to cross wide rivers, such as the Teme at Ludlow and the Severn at Bewdley for example, they were carried on bridges, but in the case of the Wye near Ddole Farm, they were buried under the bed of the river. However, in 1952 the River Claerwen, a tributary of the Elan, was dammed to provide an additional resource, and in 1969 a fourth main was added, also 60in in diameter. This one was carried over the Wye by the bridge which can be seen today, while the three older pipes remain out of sight underground.

After the reorganisation of the water industry in 1973 the Elan Valley complex was transferred from the Birmingham Corporation to the newly created Dŵr Cymru (Welsh Water), but in 1983 the Severn Trent Authority assumed responsibility for the aqueduct and they now own Ddole bridge, while the dams remain under the control of Dŵr Cymru.

There are rights of way along both banks of the river. One leads from **Felindre (19)** along the left bank, but probably the easiest way is to take the bridle path along the right bank upstream from Ddole. The bridge itself is fenced off so visitors cannot use it to cross the river.

(CJ, ES, WJS)

DDOLE   Sixty-inch water pipeline added to the Elan to Birmingham aqueduct in 1969. Three earlier pipes are under the river bed.

21 GLYN   Disused bridge of the former Mid-Wales Railway

Map 1; 136/147; 969; SN 967 657

THIS IS THE SECOND of the five bridges of the Mid-Wales Railway across the Wye (see **Cwmcoch (13)**), and the only one still reasonably intact except that the single line track has been removed. Compared with the others it is a short bridge of only one span, measuring 23m. It is a through bridge of riveted plate-girder construction with the upper flanges gently sloped up to the centre of the span and known as a hogback. Instead of sleepers, the chairs were fixed to longitudinal timber baulks which are still in place supported on transverse steel joists with diagonal bracing; walkways of planking are laid across the joists.

The bridge is situated 100m above the confluence with the River Elan. Although the flow of the Elan was reduced by about two-thirds following the construction of the dams, there is an obligation to maintain a minimum of 'compensatory' water, and the flow of the Wye below the confluence is still considerably greater than that above.

The bridge is now private property but can be reached by the minor road from Rhayader which terminates at Glyn Farm on the right bank. The approach embankment on the left bank closely follows the A470 and is sometimes used by walkers, but it is not a right of way, and the walkways over the bridge are in a dangerous condition.

(BRIS)

GLYN   A single-span plate-girder bridge of the former Mid-Wales Railway; it escaped demolition after the line was closed in 1962.

22 GLASLYN   Private footbridge

Map 1; 136/147; 969; SN 972 652

THIS IS A 'SWING' BRIDGE similar in principle to that at **Dernol (9)**, but older and with some differences. There are two pairs of main cables over each tower and each is anchored to the deck at different distances from the tower, but the wooden deck is additionally supported on cables as at Dernol. The wooden towers are surmounted by decorative ironwork, but the bridge is not so robustly constructed. It was probably built in the 1890s but has been substantially rebuilt twice, once in about 1935 and a second time in the 1960s, but the original design has apparently been preserved.

In about 1890 William Henry Banks Davis RA (1833-1914) acquired some sixty acres of land on both sides of the River Wye, and built on the left bank a substantial house with adjoining studio, which he named 'Glaslyn'. He was a successful and prolific landscape and animal painter, and in his time exhibited over one hundred works at the Royal Academy. He painted scenes in Scotland and France but in his later life he was particularly attracted to the Wye Valley, and from 1886 his subjects are increasingly from this part of Wales. The locations of many of his Welsh scenes can be identified, and in particular some can be recognised as from the right bank at Glaslyn. Although none is known to show the bridge, there is no doubt that Davis had it built so that he could cross the river, and there are several views of the hill Ceirig Gwynion upstream from Glaslyn which must have been painted within a few feet of the end of the bridge. (It is also recorded that he was a keen angler.)

Glaslyn is strictly private property and there is no public access to the bridge. (CIA, CW, NRH)

GLASLYN   A 'swing' suspension bridge on a private estate.

23 LLANWRTHWL   Connecting the village on the right bank with the A470 along the left bank

Map 1; 147; 969; SN 976 640

BUILT IN 1980, this is a simple bridge of three spans, the centre one longer than the other two, and the whole totalling 52m in length. The width is 7.5m. The concrete deck is supported on inverted U-beams of prestressed concrete with angled slab piers and concrete abutments. Its predecessor was built about 1930 of reinforced-concrete beams, and had four equal spans totalling 45m, with concrete angled piers and masonry abutments.

   Llanwrthwl is the location of a long-distance heavy vehicle transport fleet, and the deck slab was found to be too thin and inadequately reinforced to carry this load safely - it included timber from local forests - though it was able to support the lighter traffic in use when it was first built.

   There are no rights of way here but the bridge can be conveniently viewed from the road.

(HR, PCA, PHD)

LLANWRTHWL   A prestressed concrete bridge built in 1980, seen from the right bank.

The earlier concrete bridge built *c*1930 and demolished in the late 1970s because of deterioration.

Powys Highways Department

24 NANT-Y-CRAIG Site of demolished bridge, former Mid-Wales Railway

Maps 1/2; 147; 969; SO 983 628

NANT-Y-CRAIG is the name by which the bridge site is known locally. It is said to be a corruption of Glanrhydgrech, the name of the estate on both sides of the river through which the railway ran, and the name by which it was officially known by the railway. Neither of these names is shown on the Ordnance Survey map, and it seems likely that the local railwaymen called it Doldowlod, after the station 500m up the line towards Rhayader. But this name confuses with the three bridges on the Doldowlod estate, **(25)**, **(26)**, and **(27)**, downstream from the bridge, and so the name known to the local people seems to be the best one to use.

It was a 5-span bridge of parallel flanged girders with a total length of about 74m. The piers were of cast-iron cylinders grouped in threes as at **Brynwern (30)**, but in the 1920s they were encased in concrete as can be seen at **Cwmcoch (rail) (13)**; but unlike Cwmcoch, the piers were removed when the bridge was demolished after the closure of the line at the end of 1962. The outlines of the sheet piling used when the piers were enclosed in concrete can be seen when the water is low. As originally built in about 1864, the spans were probably of lattice-girder construction.

There are no rights of way leading to the bridge site, but the track bed of the railway along the embankment leading to the left bank abutment is in use. It can be reached through the caravan park (open during the summer) which is on the site of the former Doldowlod railway station.

(BRIS, RWK, TRP)

NANT-Y-CRAIG   Site of bridge on the former Mid-Wales Railway demolished after closure of the line in 1962, looking upstream.

25, 26, 27 DOLDOWLOD ESTATE

EARLY IN THE NINETEENTH CENTURY, James Watt, the celebrated engineer, bought a farmhouse near the River Wye situated on the left bank a mile below the village of Doldowlod. His son, also James, inherited the property in 1819 and greatly enlarged the estate by acquiring land on both sides of the river. He built Doldowlod House about 1827, and an extension to replace the farmhouse was added in 1878, designed by S.W. Williams who designed the first **Brynwern Bridge (30)**. It is still occupied by the Gibson-Watt family, descendants of James Watt. There are three bridge sites across the river on the estate:

25 Careg-yn-fol (SN 995 624) was a suspension footbridge opposite Doldowlod House, and built early in the present century to link the house with Careg-yn-fol, the home farm. All that can be seen today are the footings on each bank. The house can be glimpsed through the trees.

26 Ystrad (SO 002 616) is an elegant suspension bridge built in about 1880, the ironwork having been made at the Llanidloes Railway Foundry. The four-legged towers are 4.4m high built up from separate castings bolted together, and the chains are eyed rods linked by bolts, seven at the anchors, diminishing to five at the towers and two at the centre of the bridge. The length of the span between towers is 42m and the width of the deck is about 1.2m. This is a generous width for a private footbridge but not enough for a horse and cart or motor vehicle; it was built to drive livestock across the river. In 1962 the bridge was damaged by a floating tree and was repaired, but in 1989 it was completely dismantled and restored by Hope & Son of Newbridge-on-Wye. The bridge is registered by the Institution of Civil Engineers as a National Heritage structure.

27 Ty'n-y-lôn (SO 008 608) was probably identical with Careg-yn-fol and built about the same time. It provided a connection between the estate on the left bank with pheasant hatcheries located in Ty'n-y-lôn wood on the right bank. Only the stanchions for anchoring the suspension cables remain today.

There is no public access to bridges on the estate. The Wye Valley Walk follows the right bank of the river at a distance, and the track of the former Mid-Wales Railway provides *bona fide* access to Ystrad Farm, but the bridge should not be visited without permission from the occupant of the farm.
(DH, JGW, KK2, NRH, RH, WJS)

YSTRAD   A stock suspension bridge on the Doldowlod estate dating from about 1880.

CAREG-YN-FOL   Site of footbridge to Doldowlod
House glimpsed through the trees on the far side.

TY'N-Y-LÔN   Remains of a footbridge
used by the gamekeeper.

28 NEWBRIDGE-ON-WYE, rail   Site of demolished bridge, former Mid-Wales Railway

Map 2; 147; 992; SO 013 588

THIS DEMOLISHED BRIDGE was the fourth of the five bridges on the former Mid-Wales Railway which crossed the Wye on its route from Llanidloes to Three Cocks (see **Cwmcoch (rail) (13)**). It was almost identical with **Nant-y-Craig (24)**, the next bridge upstream, having spans of parallel flanged girders instead of plate girders, and piers of cast-iron cylinders grouped in threes and encased in concrete. But unlike Nant-y-Craig, it had only four spans instead of five and totalled about 60m in length compared with 74m for the other bridge. The state of the bridge today is similar to that of Nant-y-Craig, with crumbling masonry abutments largely obscured by vegetation, and a long approach embankment on the right bank. The piers were removed when the bridge was demolished after the line was closed in 1962, but when the water is low the base of the sheet piling can be seen which was used when the cast-iron piers were encased in concrete. The original spans of the bridge when it was built in about 1864 were probably lattice girders.

A right of way leads from the Beulah road, B4358, at the edge of the village before the road reaches the river, descending to the left bank which it follows upstream for 500m as far as the left bank abutment.

(BRIS, RWK, TRP)

NEWBRIDGE-ON-WYE, rail   Site of a bridge on the former Mid-Wales Railway. The right bank abutment and the approach embankment are overgrown with trees.

29 NEWBRIDGE-ON-WYE, road   Carrying B4358 from Llandrindod Wells to Beulah and Llanwrtyd Wells

Map 2; 147; 992; SO 013 582

NEWBRIDGE has long been an important crossing of the Wye linking north-east Wales and Shropshire with South Wales, and over the years there has been a succession of bridges here. The present one dates from 1981 and is a stark structure of three spans with a continuous hollow slab superstructure supported on slab piers, and all, including the abutments, made of reinforced concrete poured *in situ*. The total length is 50m and the width 10.3m. The engineers were L.G. Mouchel & Partners.

The technique of embedding iron rods or mesh in poured concrete in order to strengthen it was developed in France over a century ago, and was introduced into England by L.G. Mouchel who opened an office in London in 1897. So when a replacement bridge was planned for the Wye at Newbridge early in the present century, it was decided that it should be built of reinforced-concrete, or 'ferrocrete' as it was then called, and Mouchel was engaged as consultant. It was opened in 1911, the first reinforced concrete bridge to be built across the Wye. It had three spans, but these were gently arched with masonry piers and half-cylindrical cutwaters. The base of the railings was supported by a row of brackets which, as well as being functional, made a pleasing adornment to the whole structure. By 1972 the concrete was crumbling and in 1978 the problem was diagnosed as due to inadequate reinforcing. Sadly this elegant and historic bridge had to be demolished.

The bridge replaced a wooden one which had been in existence for many years. It was constructed entirely with timbers, having six piers each of a single row of piles driven into the river bed and connected together with boarding, thus presenting a minimum resistance to the river current.

It is not known when the bridge was built, but it had probably received many rebuilds, partially or wholly. (The central arch was reportedly carried away by a flood *c*1830). The first definite record of a bridge at Newbridge is on Saxton's map of 1610, and Leland in his *Itinerary* of 1543 also refers to a bridge, but it is not clear whether this was at Newbridge or Rhayader. The first bridge took the place of a ford which was probably used by the Romans.

The commemorative stone from the 1911 bridge is still preserved by the roadside. The Wye Valley Walk, following the valley on the side of the right bank, here uses the B4358 for a short distance, and approaches the bridge to within 100m before turning off to continue its way without crossing the river. (CVL, HT, PCA, PHD)

NEWBRIDGE-ON-WYE, road   Reinforced-concrete bridge which in 1981 replaced the earlier bridge illustrated below.

This elegant bridge built in 1911 was the first reinforced-concrete bridge on the Wye.

Powys County Archives Office

30 BRYNWERN BRIDGE   Minor country road from A470 and Newbridge-On-Wye

Map 2; 147; 992; SO 011 566

THE PRESENT BRIDGE is a simple 3-span structure with prestressed concrete beams of U section, a concrete deck and slab piers. Its total length is 52m and its width is 7.5m, and it was built in 1980 to replace a much more interesting bridge, the remains of which can still be seen alongside.

This was a 3-span lattice-girder bridge with cast-iron piers built in 1885, but it had been closed to traffic prior to the new bridge being built because of its poor condition. It had a number of interesting features, but in spite of its being listed Grade II it was demolished. Fortunately, Mr Jim Groucott of Rhayader, an industrial archaeologist, made a detailed study of the bridge before it was demolished, and it is due to him that the old masonry abutments and some of the ironwork features have been preserved as a reminder.

It was built as a toll bridge in place of a ford, and was promoted by W. Clifton Mogg, a retired clergyman of some means. The engineering was by Stephen W. Williams, a local architect and man of parts who designed several churches in the area, as well as the bridge over the Wye at **Bridge Sollers (43)** near Hereford. The contractors were William Thomas's Railway Works at Llanidloes who almost certainly built the bridges for the Mid-Wales Railway which ran from Moat Lane to Brecon and which passed through Llanidloes. An unusual feature of the bridge was the structure of the piers which consisted of narrow cast-iron columns grouped in threes and held together with triangular castings. Opposite piers were linked by crossed sway-braces attached to the columns by cast-on lugs. The lattice girders were supported directly by two of the three columns, while the third outer column took its share of the stress through cast-iron decorative braces of an unusual design bolted on to a vertical component of the lattice girder. Groucott points out that many of the now demolished railway bridges in the Wye Valley show evidence of similar triangular clustered piers which suggests a common origin with Brynwern, though they were subsequently encased in concrete. However, these bridges were built in the 1860s whereas the style at Brynwern is archaic for the 1880s, especially the use of cast-iron lugs, and Groucott believes that Clifton Mogg may have used the earlier drawings of the railway foundry as an economy measure. Also, the earlier style of the decoration might have been more to the taste of these ecclesiastically minded gentlemen. The old toll house still stands on the right bank but is not in use today.

(JBG1, PHD)

BRYNWERN   A prestressed-concrete bridge built in 1980 to replace the iron bridge illustrated below, both seen from the left bank.

The bridge built in 1885 showing the decorative bracing and distinctive piers of cast-iron piping.

J B Groucott

THIS IS THE FIRST RAILWAY BRIDGE, counting from the source of the river, of only three on the Wye still carrying rail traffic, out of an original nineteen, most of which were closed under the 'Beeching axe' in the 1960s. The other two still in use are **Eign Railway Bridge, Hereford (50)**, and **Chepstow Railway Bridge (76)**. It is a plate-girder structure of two spans with a massive, high, central masonry pier and masonry abutments. Each span is 30m long and 49m wide, and it carries trains which run between Shrewsbury and South Wales.

The Central Wales Railway was sanctioned in 1859 to connect with a line from Craven Arms on the Shrewsbury and Hereford Railway, and was opened to Llandrindod Wells in 1865. In the following year an extension brought it to Builth Road, 3km north-west of Builth Wells on the road to Rhayader. Here it met, but did not at that time join, the Mid-Wales Railway descending the Wye Valley on its way to Brecon and beyond (see **Cwmcoch (13)**). It was not until 1867 that its construction was continued by a high level bridge over the Mid-Wales Railway, and thence over the Wye bridge 700m farther on, eventually reaching Llandovery in 1868. Each railway maintained a station at Builth Road at their respective levels, including a luggage lift between them, but the Mid-Wales Railway closed in 1964. The Central Wales Railway was absorbed by the London and North Western Railway (later the LMS) in 1868 and was renamed the Central Wales Line, known today as the Heart of Wales line.

The Wye Valley Walk closely follows the right bank of the river upstream for many miles, passing under Builth Road railway bridge about 2.5km from Builth Wells.

(CA, RWK)

BUILTH ROAD   Plate-girder bridge of the former Central Wales Railway, now the Heart of Wales line, and still in use, looking upstream.

32 BUILTH WELLS, Wye Bridge   Trunk road bridge
carrying A470 and A483

Map 2; 147; 992; SO 042 512

ALTHOUGH BUILTH WELLS is important historically as well as being a market town and a former spa resort, its greatest importance arises from its location as a river crossing. There are five major routes converging on the bridge: the A470 from Llandudno in the north and from Cardiff in the south, and the A483 from Chester in the north-east and from Swansea in the south-west, both roads crossing each other on the bridge; and in addition there is the A481 which links with the A44 from Worcester and beyond in the east, as well as local roads. Prior to 1974 the river separated Radnorshire on the north from Breconshire on the south, with Builth on the right bank in Breconshire, but now both sides of the river are in Powys.

The present bridge was built in 1779 by James Parry of nearby Hay. It has six three-centred masonry arches - they are slightly flattened at the top - which increase gradually in size towards the centre of the bridge, both of which features, though subtle, give it a distinctive profile. (Of the other Wye bridges still in existence, only **Kerne Road Bridge (60)** and the old iron bridge at **Chepstow (74)** have graduated arches.) Cutwaters were added in 1820, the central one on each side extending up to the parapet to provide a refuge, the upstream one carrying a commemorative stone. By 1910 the congestion of traffic across the bridge had become a problem, and Builth Urban District Council applied to the Breconshire Council to take a hand in widening it, but it was not until 1925 that the two counties co-operated in a major programme to double the width of the bridge. This involved building reinforced-concrete arches faced with masonry, and in 1975 a programme of further strengthening took place in which the masonry arches were supported with concrete saddles, and the customary rubble filling of the spandrels was replaced with concrete. The present dimensions are 84m in total length and 9.2m in width. The structural changes have not impaired the external appearance of the bridge. It remains one of the most elegant on the Wye.

There was evidently a footbridge in the latter part of the 13th century near a ferry and Leland in the 16th century refers to Builth as being the first place on the Wye above Hereford to have a bridge. In 1740 a wooden bridge, the third within living memory at the time, was destroyed by flood and replaced with a much stronger one with seventeen pillars, presumably built of wood, but it too was frequently damaged by ice. Not until the present stone bridge was built did Builth have a reliable crossing of the river.
(EJ, PCA, PHD, DEO)

BUILTH WELLS   A splendid masonry bridge with six three-centred arches, built in 1779 and widened in 1925, viewed downstream.

The bridge *c*1820 from an engraving by William Radclyffe (1780-1855) after David Cox the younger (1809-1885).

Monmouth Museum

33 ERWOOD   B4594 connecting A470 on the right bank with Painscastle

THE BRIDGE IS LOCATED about 1km upstream from Erwood village and, as can be read on a plaque attached to the railings, was built in 1967 under the joint authority of the county councils of Brecon and Radnor, at that time the respective counties on either side of the river. Tarmac Civil Engineering Limited was the contractor. It has four composite spans of steel beams and a reinforced-concrete slab deck supported on piers of twin octagonal concrete columns, and with concrete abutments. The total length is 85m and the width 7.3m, and the deck is about 9m above the river bed.

   The bridge was located just below an earlier one built in 1877 which was then demolished. This was a toll bridge of lattice-girder construction supported on piers, one on each side of the bridge, each pier consisting of three cast-iron columns braced together in a triangle, two in line with and supporting the lattice girder, and the third outside the line of the bridge and carrying a decorative brace attached to the lattice (see also illustration to **Brynwern Bridge (30)**). The bridge, including the masonry abutments which can still be seen, is almost identical with Brynwern Bridge except that it had four spans whereas Brynwern, built in 1885, eight years later than Erwood, had only three. Brynwern was designed by S.W. Williams, a celebrated local architect, and constructed by William Thomas's Railway Foundry at Llanidloes, and there is little doubt that Erwood bridge has a similar origin. (Thomas also constructed the bridges for the Mid-Wales Railway, opened in 1864, and they too originally had similar piers: **Cwmcoch (13)** and **Newbridge-on-Wye (28)** as well as others on the Dulas and the Ithon.) When the water is low enough, the footings and stubs of some of the pier columns can still be seen; and the old toll house, close to the left bank abutment, is still in use as a residence. 'Erwood' is said to be a corruption of the Welsh 'Y Rhyd' meaning a ford, and it used to be an important crossing for the Welsh drovers taking their cattle to the English markets.

   The Wye Valley Walk crosses the river by Erwood Bridge, following the old Mid-Wales Railway line along the left bank downstream to **Llanstephan Bridge (34)** and upstream from the right bank over the high ground to Builth Wells. A right of way also exists along the left bank upstream, rejoining the old railway line leading to the spectacular Aberedw Rocks and beyond.
(EJ, JBG1, PCA, PHD, RSa)

ERWOOD   A bridge of steel beams with concrete deck and piers, built in 1967 to replace the iron bridge illustrated below.

The original bridge of 1877 with lattice girders and piers of cast-iron piping.   *G Brinwant-Jones collection*

34 LLANSTEPHAN   Minor road connecting A470 on the right bank with Llanstephan, and along the left bank to Boughrood

Map 2; 161; 1015; SO 112 416

LLANSTEPHAN is the only vehicular suspension bridge on the Wye*, but in 1994 it was closed to traffic pending replacement of the cables which had corroded rendering the bridge unsafe.

It is an attractive bridge, built in 1922 by David Rowell & Company of Westminster. It is suspended from a pair of cables on each side, separated by links to which the suspenders are attached. The lattice-work towers are capped with decorative spikes and connected near the top with substantial cross-diagonal bracing; and the deck consists of transverse timbers without asphalt topping. The total length is 80.5m but it is only 2.3m wide. There is a cast-iron plaque at each end of the bridge announcing that 'the moving load on this bridge must not exceed a total weight of five tons on four wheels at a speed of not more than 4 miles per hour'. The plaque, which dates from the inception of the bridge, is small and mostly hidden by vegetation, but prominent modern signs reduce the total permissible weight to 2 tons and prudently limit traffic to one vehicle at a time; in fact it is not easy for cars and pedestrians to pass each other.

The Wye Valley Walk crosses Llanstephan Bridge, following the right bank closely downstream for 4km to **Boughrood Bridge (35)**, and along the dismantled Mid-Wales Railway track near the left bank upstream for about the same distance to **Erwood Bridge (33)**.

(PHD)

*The term 'suspension bridge' is used in the strict sense of being suspended from a flexible connection reaching from one side of the river to the other. The Wye section of the **Severn Bridge (77)** is more correctly defined as a cable-stayed bridge.

LLANSTEPHAN   An elegant narrow vehicular suspension bridge built in 1922, looking upstream.

35 BOUGHROOD, road B4530 connecting A470 on the right bank with Boughrood and Glasbury on the left bank

Map 2; 161; 1038; SO 130 384

SITUATED 500m UPSTREAM from Llyswen on the right bank, Boughrood Bridge is the youngest masonry-arched bridge on the Wye. In 1834 parliament was petitioned by Walter Wilkins and other prominent landowners for a bridge to replace an existing ferry. Wilkins (later de Winton) had previously owned the ferry and was at that time building the family seat at Maesllwch Castle in nearby Glasbury. The bridge was opened as a toll bridge in 1842. It consists of four massive segmental arches on piers with rounded cutwaters on both sides and thin buttresses extending up to the parapet. In addition there are two smaller semicircular flood arches, one on each bank. Later, a toll house was incorporated in the downstream side on the left bank abutment, now a private residence. The bridge was widened in 1956, its present dimensions being 99m in total length and 5.8m in width.

There are several rights of way between Glasbury and Boughrood including the Wye Valley Walk. The latter crosses the bridge and follows the right bank closely upstream for 4km to **Llanstephan Bridge (34)**.

(BLG, DD, PHD, RH)

BOUGHROOD, road   A massive masonry bridge with four main segmental arches widened in 1956, looking upstream.

36 BOUGHROOD, rail   Site of demolished Mid-Wales Railway bridge

Map 2; 161; 1038; SO 132 386

THIS IS THE LAST of the five bridges of the Mid-Wales Railway which crossed the Wye on its way downstream. The line was opened in 1864 and closed in 1962 (see **Cwmcoch (13)**). Like the bridge at **Glyn (21)** it consisted of a single span, but unlike Glyn, which is still in existence, it was demolished after the line was closed, and all that remains today are the masonry abutments. It was a lattice-girder through bridge with a span of 46m, and in 1951 it was strengthened by reinforcing the ironwork. This span is believed to have replaced an earlier one of lighter construction, possibly in the 1920s when the iron piers of some of the other bridges, such as Cwmcoch, were strengthened with concrete. Formerly the abutments carried massive masonry pillars supporting the ends of the girders, but these were removed at the time of the reinforcement work. The lower photograph shows this work in progress.

The bridge is situated only 300m to the north-east of **Boughrood Road Bridge (35)**, but it crosses the river 1km downstream, because at Llyswen, on the right bank, the river doubles back on itself and the bridge crosses it at the head of its return loop. The former Boughrood station, 300m north of the bridge, was renamed 'Boughrood and Llyswen' in 1912, as it served both villages: Boughrood on the left bank in former Radnorshire and Llyswen on the other side in former Breconshire.

The B4350 to Glasbury, which leaves the A420 and crosses the river by Boughrood road bridge, passes close to the left bank abutment of the railway bridge. It formerly crossed over the railway by an 'under bridge' - i.e. at an elevated level - but with the removal of the railway track after the closure, the bridge and its approach embankment was also removed, and the road is now at ground level.

There are some rough steps used by anglers leading down from the road to the left bank from which the abutments on both sides can be seen, otherwise the remains of the bridge are largely hidden from view.

(GBJ, RWK)

BOUGHROOD, rail   Site of demolished single-span bridge of the old Mid-Wales Railway, the right bank abutment almost hidden by trees.

The bridge in 1951 when the latticework was strengthened and the masonry pillars removed.

Welsh Industrial and Maritime Museum

37 GLASBURY   A438 between Hereford and Brecon

Maps 2/3; 161; 1038; SO 179 392

THIS SPLENDID MAIN ROAD BRIDGE of six spans is by far the longest in the upper part of the Wye Valley. Its total length is 120m, and only those near the mouth of the river at Chepstow - **New Road Bridge (75)**, **Railway Bridge (76)** and the **Wye Section, Severn Bridge (77)** - are longer. The railway bridge at **Monmouth, Troy (WVR) (67)** (now dismantled) was also a little longer if its approach viaduct, which still stands, is included.

Built in 1923 it has gently arched beams and a deck of reinforced concrete supported on masonry piers. It has been rebuilt twice, the first time in 1964 when it was widened on both sides and redecked, and the second in 1989 when it was again widened, but only on the upstream side. Its present width is 11m.

Glasbury seems to have had a succession of bridges in the past. There was a wooden one which was washed away in 1738, and another, built by William Edwards of Pontypridd, which suffered the same fate in 1777 and was replaced by a stone bridge of seven arches; but this too was destroyed by flood in 1795. Formerly, although Radnorshire largely occupied the left bank of the river and Breconshire the right, there was a detached area of Radnorshire amounting to about 470 acres on the right bank, and the responsibility for the maintenance of the bridge lay wholly with Radnorshire. However in 1832, following the Parliamentary Reform Act, the detached area was transferred for electoral purposes only to Breconshire which nevertheless refused to accept responsibility for the adjoining half of the bridge. As a consequence, by 1847 a wooden bridge which had replaced the previous stone one had become unsafe, and it was only after protracted litigation that Breconshire agreed to share the cost, and the bridge was rebuilt in 1850, the Breconshire half by the right bank with stone piers and the Radnorshire half by the other of wood. The latter can be seen on the left in the lower photograph. This one seems to have stood up to the onslaught of the Wye floods until the present bridge was built.

The Wye Valley Walk follows the left bank above and below the bridge, but for some reason it diverts through the village of Glasbury though there is a right of way along the bank between the village and the river. Glasbury Bridge is the upper limit to which boats may legally travel without obtaining permission from the riparian owners.

(EJ, KK2, PHD, RH, RSa)

GLASBURY   A magnificent multi-span bridge of reinforced concrete built in 1923 on earlier masonry piers, seen from the left bank.

The earlier bridge of 1850 seen from the right bank showing wooden piers on the far, Radnorshire, half of the river.   *Monmouth Museum*

38 HAY-ON-WYE   B4351 between the A438 at Clyro and Hay-on-Wye

Map 3; 161/148; 1016; SO 228 426

HAY-ON-WYE, just inside the Welsh boundary, has always been important as a border town and more recently as a bookselling centre. The bridge is vital, as the town is situated on the right bank of the river, whereas the main A438 between Hereford and Brecon follows the valley on the opposite side.

The present bridge was built in 1957. It has six spans of prestressed-concrete beams supported high above the river on twin concrete pillars. Its total length is 117m and its width 10m, nearly as long as **Glasbury (37)**, its upstream neighbour; but it is not so attractive visually as its tall and relatively slender pillars give an appearance of instability. It replaced an iron bridge of similar design dating from 1868 with lattice girders and twin spidery pillars. At that time the Hereford, Hay and Brecon Railway was being built, following an earlier horse-drawn tramway along the right bank of the river, but the Board of Trade would not allow the railway to cross the approach road to the bridge at the same level. So the railway contractor, Thomas Savin, agreed to build the new bridge at a higher level at his own expense in return for a 99-year lease of the tolls. The railway was closed in 1964, but its former existence explains why the present bridge is so high.

The first bridge was built in 1763 under an Act of Parliament of 1756 which empowered commissioners to collect tolls for its maintenance. It had five masonry arches and was built at a much lower level than the present bridge, but in 1795 three of the arches on the Hay side were washed away in the floods which also destroyed the bridges at **Glasbury (37)** and **Whitney (40)**. They were replaced with five timber piers which lasted until 1855 when they were again destroyed. However, the bridge was repaired, but it remained in a dangerous state until the high-level iron bridge was opened three years later.

In 1861, the bridge was a scene of severe rioting. Because the collection of tolls had been granted to the builder in the first instance for 99 years, it had been assumed by the people that thereafter the bridge would be free. It was only when confronted with the original Act of Parliament that the crowd accepted the fact that the tolls would continue, which they did until 1933.

Offa's Dyke Path and the Wye Valley Walk meet at Hay-on-Wye, both using the bridge to cross the river as well as each other. There is also a right of way along the right bank which follows the route of the disused railway under the bridge for some distance.

(EJ, JM, KK2, RH)

HAY-ON-WYE   A prestressed-concrete bridge perched on top of tall cylindrical columns, built in 1957, looking downstream.

A drawing of Hay bridge before 1815 by James Bourne showing wooden piers built after damage by flood in 1795.

National Library of Wales

39 WHITNEY-ON-WYE   Dismantled railway bridge, Hereford, Hay and Brecon Railway

Map 3; 148; 1016; SO 258 475

THE HEREFORD, HAY AND BRECON RAILWAY was incorporated in 1859. As finally built, it followed the Wye Valley up from Hereford to Hay, and thence to Three Cocks near Glasbury where it joined the Mid-Wales Railway coming down the valley, and from where it had running powers on to Brecon. The HHBR became part of the Midland Railway and later of the LMS, while the MWR was absorbed by the Great Western Railway. Whereas the MWR crossed the Wye by five bridges (see **Cwmcoch (13)**), the HHBR needed only one, here at 'Whitney-on-the-Wye' as it was grandiloquently named. The village and the site of its former railway station lie 1.2km along the road towards Hereford. The line was opened for traffic in 1864.

There had been a predecessor named the Hay Railway, which was a 3ft 6in gauge horse-drawn tramway running between Brecon and Eardisley, and which was completed in 1818. It was obliged to cross the river by **Whitney toll bridge (40)** as the bridge owners had sole rights to the crossing over that stretch of the river. The new railway company bought the tramway and replaced its narrow-gauge flanged rails with standard-gauge track. However, when it came to crossing the river it had of necessity to build a more suitable bridge of its own, but it had to pay compensation to the toll bridge owners. The bridge was built on a skew of about 50°, 60m upstream from the toll bridge on the left bank and 140m upstream on the right. The exact construction of the original bridge is not known, but Kilvert, in his diary entry for 11 November 1878, observes that 'the Whitney iron railway bridge was carried away last night by flood and 2 miles of line seriously damaged. No trains can run for 3 months, during which time the gap will be filled by coaches'. The subsequent bridge had three iron lattice-girder spans supported on iron columns, and a skew length over the river of about 70m. The abutments on each bank were massive masonry structures each in two halves separated by a spanned gap through which ran a road - a farm track along the right bank, and the main road to Hereford (later the A438) along the left.

The line was closed in 1962, and the bridge was subsequently dismantled. All that remains today is the right bank abutment, and the lower courses of masonry either side of the car park near the toll house on the left bank. After the bridge was dismantled, a section of the approach embankment on the left bank was removed to allow realignment on the A438, and a short stretch of the old road is now a car park.

The remaining abutment can be seen clearly from the toll bridge rising from its surrounding overgrowth of trees looking from a distance like a medieval towered castle. It can be reached by a path leading down to the river bank from the toll bridge approach, but this is not a public right of way.
(AHL, BRIS, CA, FBE2, KD)

WHITNEY-ON-WYE, rail   Site of the dismantled bridge on the former Hereford, Hay and Brecon Railway looking upstream. The bridge was on the skew, with the left bank abutment just beyond the steps on the right, and the prominent right bank abutment farther upstream on the left.

40 WHITNEY Toll Bridge   B4350 between A438 and Hay-on-Wye

Map 3; 148; 1016; SO 258 474

THIS IS ONE of the most interesting bridges on the river. It is the only toll bridge in private hands, and its unusual combination of both timber and stone spans is curious. It is the fourth bridge at this site and was built in 1802, though it has frequently had substantial repairs. With three timber spans and two semicircular stone arches, its total length is 40.7m. and the road is 4.3m wide. The timber piers are founded on stone bases and diagonal timbers give additional support to the timber deck, which has a macadamised surface.

In 1818, the Hay Railway was opened between Hay and Eardisley. This was a horse-drawn tramway which was intended to cross the Wye at Whitney by a new iron bridge, but the owners of the toll claimed exclusive rights of crossing at this point, and the tramway company was obliged to lay its track across the toll bridge. It was not until 1863 that the Hereford, Hay and Brecon Railway obtained their Act to replace the tramway, and to build a new railway bridge, **Whitney-on-Wye (rail) (39)**, but they had to guarantee the tolls on the old bridge up to £345 a year, a situation which obtained until the closure of the railway at the end of 1962.

This stretch of the river seems to have been particularly capricious, with devastating floods at some times and fordable passages at others, and the river changed its course on at least two occasions. The second was in 1730 when at Whitney the river moved to its present course from one 700m to the south, and the old church on the left bank found itself on the other side. A ferry was established 150m downstream from where the present bridge stands, but in 1774 the populace agitated for a bridge, and a Bill for this purpose was presented to Parliament in that year and duly passed. Three bridges were then built in quick succession, the first two soon being washed away, but the third lasted until 1795 when it, too, succumbed to a record flood which also destroyed the bridges at **Glasbury (37)** and **Hay (38)**. All three were of similar construction, having five stone arches each of 9m span and a width of 3.6m. The third bridge built in 1782 is shown here in an illustration which is taken from a pencil and wash sketch by James Wathen in 1787. Engineers who have examined the stone arches of the present bridge think it probable that they are in fact the end arches of the third bridge.

There is no toll for pedestrians, and there is a right of way across the meadow on the right bank downstream from the bridge from which it can be viewed from a distance.

(FBE1, FBE2, HWHP, WJS)

WHITNEY-ON-WYE toll bridge   Famous for its mixture of timber and masonry spans and dating from *c*1802, it is here viewed looking upstream.

A drawing of 1787 by James Wathen (1751-1828) of the previous bridge, largely washed away in 1795.

Hereford and Worcester County Libraries

41 BREDWARDINE   Minor road connecting the village with Brobury and A438

Map 3; 148/149; 1016; SO 337 447

BREDWARDINE BRIDGE is the only one on the Wye built of brick, and E. Jervoise, in his study of ancient bridges in Wales and western England, considered it to be one of the finest of such bridges in England. It was built as a toll bridge in 1769 to replace two ferries. The tolls were removed in 1824 but reintroduced in 1863 to help the trustees with the cost of repairs. Herefordshire County Council assumed responsibility in 1894, but the toll house, on the Bredwardine side, is still in use as a cottage.

The bridge consists of six semicircular arches of equal width, four over the river and a flood arch on each of the banks. The total length is 87m and the road 40m wide and some 10m above normal water level. The cutwaters both upstream and downstream are angular, and two on each side are extended up to the parapet to provide refuges. This good design and sound construction has served it well as it is the only bridge on the upper Wye to have survived the great flood of 1795 which destroyed the bridges at **Glasbury (37)**, **Hay (38)** and **Whitney (40)**, though it did need substantial repairs. Francis Kilvert, the diarist, was vicar of Bredwardine and a trustee of the bridge. The entry in his diary for 11 November 1878 describes a great flood in which many people were washed out of their houses and spent the night on the bridge watching the waters carrying a variety of animals, dead and alive, pass underneath; and in the following month how 'huge masses and floes of ice were coming down the river all day, rearing, crushing and thundering against the bridge', evidently without ill effect on the structure, though it was reported that the iron railway bridge at **Whitney (39)** had been carried away.

However, by 1922 cracks and holes had appeared in the brickwork, and the bridge was described as 'none too secure, and greatly in need of attention'. The building of a new one was suggested, but fortunately for us it was decided instead to restore the old one thoroughly. It was almost dismantled; the loose rubble within was replaced with concrete, and the arches and piers strengthened with girders and cross-ties of reinforced concrete. The face work was then rebuilt with selected bricks exactly to the original design, and the bridge thus preserved for many more years.

A right of way on the right bank leads downstream from the bridge to the churchyard where Kilvert was buried after his premature death in 1879. (AHL, EJ, GHJ, KD, KK2, WJS)

BREDWARDINE   The beautiful red brick multi-arched bridge of 1769, rebuilt in 1922, seen from the right bank.

A close-up showing signs of neglect before the bridge was rebuilt.   *Hereford City Museum*

42 MOCCAS Site of private toll bridge between Moccas and Monnington

Map 3; 148/149; 1016; SO 364 433

FOR OVER THREE CENTURIES the Moccas estate on the south side of the Wye has been owned by the Cornewall Family and their descendants, and in 1835 it was inherited by Sir Velters Cornewall Bt. At that time the estate included Monnington on the other side of the river; and in 1867, at his expense, work commenced on building a toll bridge wide enough for wheeled vehicles which would replace the existing ferry. It was located 800m downstream from Moccas Court, a comely red brick mansion designed by Adam and built in 1775. The bridge was designed by Lane & Blount of London who were the main contractors, while the iron work was carried out by R. Laidlaw & Son of Glasgow, and the masonry by Thomas Denley of Hereford. When completed in 1869, it consisted of three spans of iron segmental arches with decorative cast-iron spandrels and similar parapets, supported on masonry piers and abutments, and there was a toll house at each end.

By the 1950s the bridge was in need of repair and it is said that the county authority offered to take responsibility for it, an offer which evidently was not accepted. However, the bridge later succumbed to the great flood of 1960-61, like so many other Wye bridges, and a floating tree caused such damage that the bridge had to be demolished. Today only the abutments remain as well as the toll houses which are still inhabited.

The short road which led to the bridge from the Moccas - Preston road is now overgrown and impassable, though the site can be approached across the fields at the back of the toll house. However, the land is private, though Moccas Court and the grounds are open to the public on Sunday afternoons during the summer. A better view of the site can be obtained from the Monnington side, though this involves a walk of 1.6km there and back. Unauthorised cars are not allowed beyond Monnington, but there is a right of way along Monnington Walk westward towards Brobury Scar, and after 400m the road to the former bridge turns off to River Cottage, the toll house on the left bank, and along the embankment to the top of the abutment.
(AHL, HWRO, KK2)

MOCCAS   Site of a private toll bridge in the grounds of Moccas Court, demolished after suffering damage in the flood of 1960-61.

The bridge was built in 1869 to link the estate on both sides of the river, and for the use of the public.

Hereford City Museum

43 BRIDGE SOLLERS   Minor road between A438 and Madley

Map 3; 148/149; 1017; SO 412 424

THIS BRIDGE, BUILT IN 1896, was designed by S.W. Williams of Rhayader, the architect and man of many parts who designed the former Wye bridges at **Brynwern (30)** and **Erwood (33)**. It is a 3-span cast-iron lattice-girder through bridge, supported on two twin cylindrical iron piers braced with diagonal stays, and with massive masonry abutments and approach parapets. The original trough deck was strengthened with reinforced concrete in 1948, and the total length is 54.3m. The bridge replaced an ancient ford, and a ferry in times of flood, which was situated about 100m upstream. The site of the ford is easily located below Knapp Farm at the end of a lane winding down from the direction of the church. On the opposite side of the river a fence from Bridge Farm continues the line of the road from Madley, where it turns sharply towards the bridge, and leads straight to the ford.

Bridge Sollers (on old maps it is spelt 'Sollars') was so named long before it had a bridge. The word is of Scandinavian origin and meant not only a river crossing but also a fixed or floating pier or wharf - 'brygge' in Norwegian today means simply a pier - and Canon Bridge, for instance, 3km farther downstream, has never had a bridge. It is thought that stone for building Hereford Cathedral may have been obtained from the significantly named Bishopstone Quarries nearby, and shipped to the city from Bridge Sollers by barge.

A public right of way follows the right bank of the river between Bridge Sollers and Canon Bridge.

(AHL, HWHP, JW, OED)

BRIDGE SOLLERS   A lattice-girder bridge built in 1896 to the design of S W Williams, the celebrated Rhayader architect, seen from the right bank.

44 KENCHESTER (Magna) Site of Roman Bridge

Maps 3/4; 148/149; 1017; SO 442 412

FOLLOWING THEIR CONQUEST OF BRITAIN, the Romans established a main road between the legionary fortresses at Chester (Deva) and Caerleon (Isca). Most of this road is recorded as Iter XII of the Antonine Itinerary, which is assumed to have been compiled in the 2nd or 3rd century AD. The route passed through Abergavenny (Gobannium), Kenchester (Magna), Leintwardine (Bravonium) and Wroxeter (Viroconium). Much of the road between these places can be recognised from aggers (embankments) and from straight alignment of existing roads, supplemented by archaeological excavation. In 1893, the meadow on the north side (left bank) of the river was trenched and the existence of the road proved there; and the site of Magna, 0.8km east of the village of Kenchester and 1.5km north of the river, has been excavated on several occasions and the presence of the road established there too. On the south side, the alignment is clearly seen from the 2km of straight road (known as Stone Street) passing close to Madley and, within recorded memory, extending as far as the river bank, though today it does not reach so far. There can therefore be no doubt about the exact location of the crossing. That it was a bridge is also beyond doubt, as the Romans were experienced bridge builders and would certainly have provided a bridge for such an important road as this. There is no evidence of any masonry, so the bridge must have been built of wood. Some timbers were reported nearby in the river in 1893, but were not convincingly shown to have been of Roman origin.

After the Romans left in about 410AD, the bridge would have fallen into disrepair as the Saxons had no skills in bridge building. Travellers would then have been diverted to an earlier road which branched off somewhere near Tillington and led to the nearest ford which was some 7km downstream. Here, in due course, a new community grew up which was to become the city of Hereford.

In the photograph, the view is looking north from the right bank. The double fence on the right follows the alignment of the Roman road, though today it marks the ancient parish boundary between Madley on this side of the fence and Eaton Bishop on the other. The road continued across the river and over the low flat hill where Old Weir Farm now stands, and thence to Magna out of sight on the other side of the hill. From here it made a half turn to the right to pass to the east of Credenhill in the distance where the profile of an iron age hill fort on the top can just be made out.

The land on both sides of the river is private, but a farm road - not a right of way - leads to the site, a distance of 1km from Lower Eaton Farm which is situated on a minor road between Eaton Bishop and Canon Bridge. (RCHM2, HCM, IDM, RSh)

KENCHESTER   Site of a Roman bridge. No trace exists of the bridge today, but the double fence on the right follows the course of the road which led to the Roman town of Magna which was situated between the farm on the hill opposite and Credenhill in the far distance.

45 HEREFORD, Hunderton Bridge   Cycletrack and footpath between Barton and Red Hill

Map 4; 149; 1040;   SO 502 393

THIS FORMER RAILWAY BRIDGE was built in 1912-13 and purchased by Hereford City Council from the Great Western Railway in 1981; the line had been closed since 1966. It is a skew bridge and has three segmental steel arches between two masonry piers, and a single-arched masonry approach on each bank. The total length is 84m and the width, designed for a double rail track, is 8m. The arches and spandrels are built up from steel plates riveted together. Painted in green picked out in yellow, and embellished with the city coat of arms, it makes an attractive feature in Hereford's riverscape.

The present bridge is a replacement for the first one which was built in 1853. It was designed by Charles Liddell, a civil engineer and architect with the GWR, and was evidently intended to resemble the original as closely as possible. However, whereas the newer bridge is of riveted steel platework, the arches of the earlier one were of wrought-iron segments bolted together, and the deck was supported by hollow rectangular cast-iron columns braced with tie-rods. The original masonry piers were used again.

In 1846 the Newport, Abergavenny and Hereford Railway was authorized. It replaced an earlier horse-drawn tramway from the Brecknock Canal near Abergavenny to Hereford, terminating on the right bank at a point now covered by the approach to Greyfriars Bridge. The new railway continued northward across Hunderton Bridge to a terminal at Barton, now the site of the Sainsbury supermarket. The curved embankment of the tramway, covered with trees, can still be seen between Greyfriars Bridge and Hunderton School, close to the point where the two routes diverged.

In 1866 a link was built between Red Hill and Rotherwas to join the Hereford and Gloucester Railway, and passenger traffic was diverted via **Eign Bridge (50)** to Barrs Court Station (the present Hereford Station). The section between Red Hill and Barton continued to handle freight traffic until its closure in 1966, but the rest of the line is still used for traffic between Hereford, Abergavenny and Newport.

There are walks in both directions along the river banks. From the south end of the bridge a footpath follows the right bank downstream to three city bridges in succession **Greyfriars Bridge (46)**, **Wye Bridge (47)**, past Bishop's Meadow to **Victoria Bridge (48)**, and thence to King George V Playing Field, one of the most attractive walks in the city. There is no riverside walk upstream along the right bank.

(CC, DAT, EGW, RSh)

HUNDERTON   A railway bridge built in 1912-13 to replace the one shown below, which it closely resembles. It is now a cycle path.

The previous bridge, built in 1853. Both views are looking upstream but from opposite banks.

Hereford City Museum

46 HEREFORD, Greyfriars Bridge A49 between Ross-on-Wye and Shrewsbury and beyond

Map 4; 149; 1040; SO 507 395

FOR OVER FOUR-AND-A-HALF CENTURIES, the old **Hereford Wye Bridge (47)** had carried all the traffic from the south across the river and into the narrow streets of the city, and by the mid-20th century an alternative bridge and a through road to relieve the congestion was overdue.

The new bridge, authorized in the early 1960s, was completed in 1966 and is named after the 13th century Franciscan Priory which used to stand outside the City wall on the left (north) bank of the river. The engineers were Considere & Partners with McMorran & Whitby the consulting architects, and the main contractors were Cementation Company Limited.

At first sight the bridge appears to consist of a single arched span of concrete and brick, with brick-supported approaches on either bank. But in fact there are seven distinct sections joined end to end. In the centre is the main span over the river with five prestressed-concrete arched beams of hollow box-section supporting a deck of reinforced-concrete slabs, all of continuous poured construction. The outer faces of this structure are hidden behind veneers of concrete with a textured surface outlining the curve of the arch and the horizontal deck, and with simulated spandrels of brickwork. The main span is joined at each end with a shorter span of similar construction, but wholly enclosed in cosmetic brickwork. The two approach sections are viaducts of reinforced-concrete cross-beams each supported on four cylindrical concrete columns and with a deck of standard prestressed-concrete beams; and beyond these at the ends of the viaducts are short sections of solid embankment. All these are enclosed in brickwork. Two 7.5m underpasses, one on each side of the river, with arched portals incorporated in the brickwork give access into and through the spaces below the viaducts for car parking and other uses, and a third 3m pedestrian passage was added in 1977 at the city end. The length of the main span is 88m and each of the smaller spans 26m. The width between parapets in 20m and the total length of the bridge is about 500m.

The underside of the main span can be seen from the riverside walk along the right (south) bank, or from the car park at the end of Greyfriars Avenue on the left (north) bank. The structure of the viaduct is visible in the gated car park off the underpass between the two public car parks at the city end of the bridge, but there is no public access to the two small spans.
(HWHP, RSh)

GREYFRIARS BRIDGE   Built in 1966, its main span is of prestressed-concrete arched beams - the brickwork spandrels are decorative.

A view upstream before the bridge was built with the traditional sight of Wye Bridge (47) and the cathedral

Author's collection

47 HEREFORD, Wye Bridge   City road between Bridge Street on the north side (left bank) and St Martin's Street on the south (right bank)

Map 4; 149; 1040; SO 508 396

THE FAMILIAR VIEW of this venerable bridge with the cathedral in the background has become a symbol for the city of Hereford. Built *c*1490, it is the oldest bridge on the river, but it has been repaired, partly rebuilt, widened or strengthened so many times that it is not easy to disentangle its structural history. It has six arches of sandstone rubble faced with ashlar, but a sharp bend in the left bank hides the first arch on the city side, and when viewed from upstream there appears to be only five. The first two are pointed arches, whereas the rest are segmental. The third arch has three ribs with a later addition under each, and the sixth has a smaller arch supporting a later one above. There are triangular cutwaters on both sides which form refuges in the parapets. The total length of the bridge is 55m and the present width (it was widened in 1826) is 7.3m. Until its neighbour, **Greyfriars Bridge (46)**, was built in 1966, the old bridge carried all the traffic through the city from north to south, and today it is still a vital link for local traffic.

When the bridge was built, it included a fortified gate at the south end, in addition to the five other gates in the medieval city wall to the north of the river, but not until the Civil War were these defences put to the test. In 1645 the city was beseiged by Cromwell's Scottish supporters and defended by a Royalist garrison under Barnabas Scudamore of Holme Lacy. The Scots succeeded in capturing the bridge gate, but the defenders blew up the third arch from the city end and the Scots withdrew when they heard that King Charles was advancing from Worcester. This episode is commemorated by a bordure of saltires on the city coat of arms. The arch was soon rebuilt but the damaged gateway was not demolished until 1782.

The present bridge was preceded by a wooden one which was in place by 1100, and there are records of royal grants of timber for its repair during the 14th century. It is thought that such a bridge would have had stone piers, and from recent research it is suggested that the builders of the present bridge may have made use of these.

The riverside walk along the right bank crosses the approach road to the bridge, and it is difficult to examine the arches in detail except from a boat. The famous view of the bridge with the Cathedral can best be obtained from the walkway over Greyfriars Bridge.

(DNB, EJ, RSh, HWHP, RCHM1)

WYE BRIDGE   Built *c*1490, it is the oldest bridge on the Wye and is seen here from the right bank. The farthest two arches are pointed, and the third is that blown up during the Civil War.

The bridge in 1785, from a drawing by James Wathen (1751-1828).   *Hereford and Worcester County Libraries*

48 HEREFORD, Victoria Bridge   Footpath between Mill Street on the left bank and Bishop's Meadow and King George V Playing Fields on the right

Map 4; 149; 1040; SO 513 394

THIS DELIGHTFUL VICTORIAN BRIDGE is in marked contrast with its solid medieval neighbour upstream, **Hereford Wye Bridge (47)**. The two bridges, so different in character, embrace between them a short but attractive stretch of the River Wye flowing unusually through urban surroundings. On the left bank to the north are the Bishop's Palace and cathedral, and the Castle Green with Castle Cliff, the latter building all that remains of the castle today; and on the right bank there is a broad riverside walk through an elegant avenue of beech trees bordering the playing fields beyond.

The bridge was opened in 1898 to commemorate the Diamond Jubilee of Queen Victoria in the previous year, and replaced a ferry which had been opened five years earlier. It is a suspension bridge with double-bar chains supported by twin lattice wrought-iron towers hinged at the bottom and resting on masonry piers. At each end are two decorative lamp standards on terracotta pedestals, and the structure is embellished with four coloured cast-iron royal coats of arms - one at each end on the towers and the others on either side in the middle of the bridge. There were once decorative finials on top of the towers but these unfortunately have disappeared. The deck, stiffened with lattice girders, was originally of timber but in 1968 it was replaced with a galvanised steel floor covered with asphalt. The bridge was designed by the city engineer, John Parker, and the ironwork was constructed by Findlay & Co of Motherwell. Its overall length is 55.4m, and its width 2.5m.

Both photographs were taken from the right bank, the lower one before the bridge was built. In the latter, the object like a sentry box is a ferryman's hut and his boat is tied up by the bank. The building off the right of both photographs is the General Hospital.
(AHL, HWHP)

VICTORIA BRIDGE   An elegant suspension footbridge opened in 1898 to celebrate Queen Victoria's Diamond Jubilee in the previous year.

The site of the bridge before it was built. The ferryman's hut, like a sentry box, and his boat can be seen.

Hereford City Museum

49 HEREFORD, Eign Bridge, sewage works   Pipelines to and from Rotherwas

Map 4; 149; 1040; SO 522 388

THE PIPES are not visible as the bridge consists of a tube of quadrangular cross-section through which they pass. Built in 1974, it is constructed of reinforced concrete in three spans and supported on slab piers. The tube is 2.4m deep by 4.6m wide at the top and 3.6m at the bottom. There are five pipes between the Eign sewage works on the left bank and a similar works at the Rotherwas Industrial Estate on the opposite side of the river. Two are for sewage to Rotherwas (one third of the total intake at Eign) and two are for treated sludge back to Eign. There is also a pipe for sewage from some factories on the Rotherwas Estate direct to Eign. The top deck of the bridge was designed to carry road traffic between the two works but British Rail would not allow the road to cross their tracks (the Hereford and Newport line), and the bridge has never been used for this purpose. It ends abruptly at the right bank where the pipes descend underground to continue their journey.

There is a right of way along the left bank of the river from the **Victoria Bridge (48)** (following the Wye Valley Walk for a short distance before it turns inland), and passing between the sewage works and the river, under the pipeline bridge, and thence to **Eign Railway Bridge (50)** where there is parking space nearby on the river bank. Alternatively there is a right of way across the fields from Green Street, Bartonsham, which joins the other before it reaches the sewage works.

(RJ)

EIGN, sewage   A concrete tubular bridge carrying sewage pipes between the Eign and Rotherwas sewage works, looking downstream.

50 HEREFORD, Eign Bridge, Rail Hereford, Abergavenny and Newport Line

Map 4; 149; 1040; SO 522 392

EIGN BRIDGE is one of only three railway bridges across the Wye which are still used as such, out of an original nineteen, the other two being **Builth Road (31)** and **Chepstow (76)**. The present structure, built in 1931, is a plate-girder through bridge with two spans. The pier consists of two cylindrical columns of riveted plates, 1.8m in diameter. The length between abutments is 48.8m, and the width is 7.9m. The approaches on both banks include semicircular flood arches built of brick, three on the broad flat right bank and one on the steeper left bank.

The first bridge at this site was built for the Hereford, Ross and Gloucester Railway which was opened in 1855 and worked by the Great Western Railway. It terminated at Barrs Court (the present Hereford station) 1.5km beyond the bridge, which was also the terminus of the Shrewsbury and Hereford Railway. This was a standard gauge line, whereas the HR&GR was a broad gauge single track line designed to connect with I.K. Brunel's South Wales Railway. On its way to Ross the HR&GR crossed the Wye at four places: not only at Hereford but also at **Ballingham (52)**, **Strangford (55)** and **Backney (57)**. All four bridges were much the same: with five or six spans of timber construction supported on stone piers (see lower photograph **(57)**).

In 1866 the HR&GR was converted to mixed gauge so that the two lines could be connected. A two-mile link was then opened between Red Hill on the Newport, Abergavenny and Hereford Railway, a double track standard gauge line terminating at Barton, and Rotherwas on the HR&GR. In order to accommodate the increased traffic the timber and stone bridge was demolished and a new double-track iron bridge was built in its place. The line to Ross and Gloucester beyond the junction at Rotherwas was abandoned in 1965.

The new bridge was similar to the present one, except that it had three unequal spans instead of two. Their lengths were 13.4m, 21.2m and 13.4m respectively, totalling 48.8m like its successor, and each of the piers consisted of three iron cylindrical columns of 1.2m diameter instead of two of 1.8m. The arched approaches were those still in use with the present bridge.

Outfall Works Road, which serves **Eign sewage works (49)** from Hampton Park Road, leads to the river bank close to the bridge, and it also meets the riverside right of way from **Victoria Bridge (48)**.

(AHL, HP, MacD, RTCE, TRP)

EIGN, rail   This plate-girder bridge on the Hereford, Abergavenny and Newport line was built in 1931 to replace the bridge shown below.

Built in 1866 to replace an earlier wooden bridge of the then Hereford, Ross and Gloucester Railway. From a contemporary print.   *Hereford City Museum*

51 HOLME LACY   B4399 connecting Hereford south of the Wye with B4224 along the left bank

Map 4; 149; 1040; SO 568 365

HOLME LACY BRIDGE crosses the river by the hamlet of Even Pits on the right bank, and is sometimes referred to by that name, whereas Holme Lacy lies 1.5km away towards Hereford. The eastward-meandering river, after leaving Hereford, meets the hills known to geologists as the Woolhope Dome between Mordiford and Even Pits and is forced from there on to meander southward instead.

The bridge, built in 1973, has three equal spans of steel beams with reinforced-concrete slabs, supported on the two masonry piers of the previous bridge. The beams were pre-flexed, i.e. they were rolled with a slight upward bend so that when emplaced they would flatten under their own weight. It was designed by engineers of the former Herefordshire County Council and built by Marples Ridgeway Limited with steelwork by Boulton & Paul Limited, its total length being 79m.

It replaced an earlier bridge built in 1878. This had three through-deck Warren girder spans with added lattice work resting on the masonry piers which support the present bridge. It was originally a toll bridge but the tolls have been abolished and the toll house which stood on the Holme Lacy side removed. Before that there was a crossing here known as Holme Ferry.

There is a right of way stretching for miles in either direction beside the river along the right bank, and another on the left bank, nearer to the road between Mordiford and Fownhope.
(AHL, HWHP, KK2)

MORDIFORD BRIDGE - The River Lugg, flowing southward, joins the Wye 700m above Holme Lacy bridge, and is crossed at Mordiford by the B4274 to Hereford 350m above that. Although not actually over the Wye it is in the Wye Valley, and it deserves a mention here as parts of it are in fact older than Wye Bridge at Hereford. It is built of masonry and consists of two main arches over the river and seven smaller ones in the causeway for floodwater and diversionary channels across the flat to the west. The western of the two main arches (pointed and with three ribs) is considered to date from at least 1352 (Hereford Wye Bridge is dated from 1490), and the others at various later dates, but the history of the many additions and alterations is complex. The Wye Valley Walk between the Woolhope Dome and Hereford is directed across Mordiford Bridge.
(EJ, RCHM2)

HOLME LACY   A steel beam bridge built in 1975 to replace the one illustrated below. The wooded hill is part of the Woolhope Dome.

The original lattice-girder bridge built in 1850 which replaced a ferry at Even Pitts.   *Hereford City Museum*

52 BALLINGHAM   Dismantled railway bridge, former Hereford, Ross and Gloucester Railway

Map 4; 149; 1040; SO 569 306

BALLINGHAM BRIDGE was the second of the four railway bridges between Hereford and Ross which crossed the River Wye (see **Hereford, Eign Railway Bridge (50)**). The line was opened in 1855, but it had taken four years to complete the 36km between Gloucester and Hereford because of the four bridges and four tunnels required along this meandering stretch of the river. Built to the broad gauge, the line was worked by the Great Western Railway, but it was converted to mixed gauge in 1866 and subsequently to standard gauge. Originally, the bridge had six timber spans with five tall masonry piers (see lower illustration **(57)**, but the timber spans were subsequently replaced (probably more than once), with plate girder spans. The total length of the bridge was 80m. The spans were removed after the line was closed in 1965, but the piers remain, proudly marching across the river as a reminder of the railway invasion nearly a century and a half ago.

On its way from Hereford, the line passed through a tunnel 1km long and then through a deep cutting of nearly similar length before crossing the bridge, after which it immediately entered another but shorter tunnel on the left bank. Ballingham station was situated in the cutting where it is crossed by the road from Ballingham to Carey, but the building has now been converted into a private residence.

A riverside right of way follows the right bank of the river upstream for 2.8km between **Hoarwithy Bridge (53)** and Ballingham Bridge, but after passing the right bank abutment of the latter it turns off, crossing a field to reach the Ballingham - Carey road.

(LO, MacD, TRP)

BALLINGHAM   View of the bridge looking upstream, dismantled after the line was closed in 1965.

View from the same bank but downstream, before the plate-girder spans were removed.

David Tipper, Patrick Rigall Collection

53 HOARWITHY   Minor road connecting the village with Kings Caple and surrounding area

Map 4; 149; 1064; SO 548 294

HOARWITHY lies on a minor road on the right bank (west side) of the river between Hereford and Ross-on-Wye. The river flows in meanders of ever increasing size, culminating in the two great loops with Kings Caple in the centre of one and Strangford in the centre of the other, and Hoarwithy lies across the river at the closed end of the Kings Caple loop. For centuries, a crossing here was important for the people of Kings Caple parish, giving access to Hereford and Ross. However, when the broad gauge Hereford, Ross and Gloucester Railway was built in 1855, providing a station at Fawley, near Kings Caple, the role of the crossing was reversed to some extent, as it enabled the people of Hoarwithy and Hentland, and their merchandise, to reach Hereford and Ross by rail.

The present bridge, the third, was opened as recently as 1990, and is constructed from steel beams with a reinforced-concrete deck. It has three equal spans totalling 77.7m, and is supported on the abutments and piers of its predecessor, with some modification. It was designed by the engineers at County Hall, Worcester, and constructed by Dean & Dyball Limited. The earlier bridge, built in 1876, had continuous truss girders with a deck of corrugated iron plates resting on top of the ironwork. Built to the design of C.W. Whitaker, consulting engineer to the bridge owners, and constructed by Westwood & Company of Poplar, London, it had the same length as the present bridge but was only 4.5m wide. It too was a toll bridge, but in 1935 the bridge company was sold to Herefordshire County Council, and the tolls were abolished. The toll cottage still stands at the Hoarwithy end.

The first bridge was authorised by an Act of Parliament of 1855 to replace a ferry, and was opened early in 1857, soon after the arrival of the railway. It had much the same dimensions as its successor, with two masonry piers, but with arched timber spans which caused trouble as they were in constant need of attention. By 1875 it was in danger of collapse, and a ferry was brought into use until the new bridge could be completed.

A right of way along the right bank downstream, and partly along the road, leads to the footbridge at **Sellack (54)**, a distance of 3.5km; or there is a shorter walk of 2.8km to the same bridge but cutting across the bend in the river and passing through Kings Caple. A third right of way follows the right bank closely upstream for 3.2km to the dismantled railway viaduct at **Ballingham (52)**.

(HH1, HWHP)

112

HOARWITHY   A steel beam bridge built in 1990 to replace the one shown below, seen from the right bank with the old toll house.

A truss-girder bridge which replaced an earlier wooden bridge in 1876, viewed from the left bank.

Hereford and Worcester County Libraries

54 SELLACK   Suspension footbridge connecting the parishes of Kings Caple on the left bank with Sellack on the right

Map 4; 149; 1064; SO 565 280

THIS INTERESTING BRIDGE was built by public subscription in 1895 to replace a ferry which had been maintained by the vicar of the combined parishes of Kings Caple and Sellack. The architect of the bridge was Ernest G. Davies MSA of Hereford, and it was built by Lewis Harper AMICE of Aberdeen. The towers are constructed from tapering iron tubes bolted to masonry bases and braced at the top with iron plaques proclaiming the name of the constructor, and enclosing the rollers for carrying the main cables. The deck consists of cross planks supported not on rigid stringers but on tensioned cables anchored at either end of the bridge, and suspended from the main cables above. The suspenders are slender rods 9mm in diameter and closely spaced at 0.6m intervals. The variation in their lengths is designed to give a marked upward curve to the deck which echoes the downward catenary of the main cables. With the suspenders barely distinguishable from one another at a distance, the effect is distinctly graceful. There are wooden kerbs along either side of the deck.

Needless to say the bridge is a right of way, and an inscribed stone on the base of the right bank tower proclaims 'To the Honour of God and the Lasting Union of these Parishes for the use of All'. The wording of the inscription hints at a certain animosity between the two parishes which is said to have prevailed before the bridge was built, but which has happily long since evaporated as the recent centenary celebrations have shown. The paths leading to and from the bridge do indeed connect the two parishes. On the right bank to the south the path crosses Sellack common and leads straight to St Tysilio's Church, and on the left bank to the north the road climbs directly up the hill to the centre of Kings Caple close to its church of St John the Baptist. The spires of both churches can be seen for miles around. That of Kings Caple is the more prominent as the church is built on a hill 40m higher than the ground on which Sellack stands, but Sellack's spire is exceptionally tall and slender.
(AHL, HWHP)

SELLACK   A suspension footbridge built in 1895 to link the villages of Kings Caple and Sellack, seen from the right bank.

55 STRANGFORD   Dismantled railway bridge, former Hereford, Ross and Gloucester Railway

Map 4; 149; 1064; SO 578 286

THIS BRIDGE, the third on the Hereford, Ross and Gloucester Railway (Great Western Railway) over the Wye, was almost identical with **Ballingham (52)**, **Backney (57)** and doubtless **Hereford, Eign Railway Bridge (49)** before the latter was rebuilt. Like these, it consisted of five masonry piers and six spans, originally of timber later replaced with plate-girder deck spans (see above references for details). But Strangford has an interesting history.

During the night of 1 March 1947 the central pier of the bridge collapsed and the spans on either side fell into the river. Fortunately no train was crossing at the time. This was during the great flood of that year - one of the highest recorded at Ross-on-Wye - and the cause was the surplus water draining along the upstream toes of the embankments and entering the river at right angles to the flow, thus scouring the foundations of the pier. The ground beneath the pier was too hard for piling, and in order to give greater freedom to the flow of the river under the bridge it was decided not to rebuild the central pier but to replace it and the collapsed spans with a single span of double length. In order to bear the additional weight, the next piers on each side were encased with reinforced concrete and streamlined cutwaters added, and a new plate-girder span of 27.7m was installed.

The line was closed in 1965 and the spans subsequently removed, but the four remaining piers, two of masonry and two encased in reinforced concrete with the double-width gap between them, are still in place as can be seen in the upper photograph. There are no rights of way to this bridge but a farm track leads from Baysham to the right bank and upstream to the bridge, a distance of 1.0km. On the left bank, the railway embankment itself has been converted to a farm lane leading from the old Fawley railway station near the west entrance to the grounds of Fawley Court. The distance to the bridge from here is 1.3km. Alternatively, a public bridle path leads eastward from Ingsbury Cottage, Kings Caple, passing through a tunnel in the railway embankment, but the lane above can be reached through gates in the neighbouring fields. The distance to the bridge by this route is 1.0km. None of these paths is open to vehicles but they are regularly used by anglers.

(GWM, MacD)

STRANGFORD   The third Wye crossing of the former HR&GR. The plate-girder spans were removed
after the line was closed in 1965.

View showing the double-length span installed after the collapse of the central pier in 1947.

David Tipper, Patrick Rigall Collection

56 FOY   Suspension footbridge between Foy and Hole-in-the-Wall

Map 4; 149; 1065; SO 604 284

THE PARISH OF FOY lies on both sides of the river: the parish church and part of the village lie in the loop of the river on the right bank (north side), and the other part, including the buildings known as Hole-in-the-Wall, are on the opposite side.

The present bridge was completed in 1921 and replaced an earlier one which was washed away by a flood in 1919. Built by Rowell & Co Limited of Westminster, it is a suspension bridge of the usual type. The towers, perhaps unusually, are constructed from two steel I-beams with cross and diagonal bracing at the top and rollers for the cables. The latter are 50mm in diameter and are anchored in concrete at either end. The transoms are of angle iron and are suspended on 19mm cables; and the deck consists of planking laid lengthways. The main span between the towers is 43.2m and of the two approach ramps that on the right bank is 15.1m and the other (on the Hole-in-the-Wall side) is 10.7m. The whole bridge is stiffened with truss girders. It is a more robust bridge than its neighbour at **Sellack (54)** upstream, and some have considered it ugly, but it is a good example of a well designed and well built small suspension bridge. Its forerunner was erected by subscription in 1876 to replace both a ford and a ferry. It was a suspension bridge and probably similar to the present one which has been described as a reconstruction.

The origin of the name Hole-in-the-Wall must frequently have caused some speculation. According to the Woolhope Club Transactions of 1922, it refers to a tunnel which was once built under the river for the convenience of two religious houses on opposite banks, but Keith Kissack considers it to be the name of a former tavern, an explanation which seems more likely.

The Wye Valley Walk does not cross the bridge but follows the road along the left bank through Hole-in-the-Wall. The bridge itself leads to several rights of way in the loop which can be used to reach the bridges at **Strangford (55)**, **Sellack (54)** and **Hoarwithy (53)**.

(AHL, HH2, HWHP, KK2)

FOY   A suspension footbridge built in 1921 to replace one washed away in 1919, seen from the left bank near Hole-in-the-Wall.

57 BACKNEY Dismantled railway bridge, former Hereford, Ross and Gloucester Railway

Map 4; 162; 1064; SO 583 271

BACKNEY is the last of the four bridges over the Wye on the Hereford, Ross and Gloucester Railway (Great Western Railway). The others are **Hereford, Eign Railway Bridge (50)** which is still in use, and **Ballingham (52)** and **Strangford (55)** which, with Backney, have been dismantled (see **(50)** for fuller details). All were originally very similar with five masonry piers supporting six spans, originally of timber, but later of plate girders. As with Ballingham and Strangford, the spans were removed after the closure of the line in 1965.

The lower photograph shows the bridge with wooden spans as originally built when the railway was opened in 1855. Although I.K. Brunel may not have been directly involved with the construction of the HR&GR, the bridge is of classic Brunel design such as he used in his South Wales and West Country railways. The longitudinal timber beams carrying the deck were supported by wooden 'raking legs' radiating from the tops of the masonry piers. These were connected by longitudinal ties usually of metal, but it is not known whether this was the case with the Wye bridges.

The left bank abutment and a section of the partly removed embankment have been landscaped and converted by the Hereford and Worcester Countryside Services into a picnic site. It adjoins Backney Common, on the road to Foy, and the area includes the river bank in front of the abutment. This makes an attractive and dramatic setting in which to examine the details of the masonry of the abutment and the five huge surviving piers of this now defunct bridge. (LGB, MacD)

BACKNEY   The piers of the fourth and last Wye crossing of the former HR&GR, opened in 1855 and closed in 1965.

An interesting photo of the bridge as originally built in about 1855 with timber spans and masonry piers.

Ian Pope Collection

58 ROSS-ON-WYE, Bridstow Bridge   A40 linking the M50 motorway with South Wales

Map 4; 162; 1064; SO 593 247

THIS BEAUTIFUL MODERN BRIDGE, designed by Scott Wilson Kirkpatrick & Partners and built by Tarmac Engineering Limited, was completed in 1960. The bridge was built as part of a new trunk road link between the Midlands and South Wales, from junction 8 on the M5 to the A40 at Wilton and forming part of the Ross bypass.

The bridge is a 3-span prestressed-concrete structure supported on two piers, one on either side of the river. These, as well as the abutments, are of reinforced concrete. The main span is 61.9m long and the two approach spans each 22.8m. The width, which includes the two-lane carriageways and a walkway on each side, is 24m.

The main span between the piers is in three parts: two end sections of 20.2m and a central section of 21.3m. Each end section is cast integrally with the adjacent approach span to form a beam supported near the centre by the pier and by the abutment at the end of the bridge, thus creating an overhanging cantilever. The central section is supported by the ends of the two cantilevers though the joins are not visible from a distance and the approach cantilever beams are anchored to the ground at the abutments. The latter are constructed with a vertical concrete wall and two triangular wing walls enclosing the fill of the approach embankments. The concrete walls are faced with masonry, but this is for appearance, and has no structural role. The abutment walls rest on a floor of concrete to which they are strongly bonded, as well as to the superstructure of the bridge above, and anchorage is provided by the weight of the embankment fill on the concrete floor. It cannot be denied that with its slender arched spans this is a bridge of considerable elegance.

There is a lay-by for vehicles at the eastern end of the bridge and there are walkways along the sides. There are also steps leading down the embankment near the left bank abutment on the upstream side by which the underside of the bridge can be reached. But the best way to see it is along the footpath following the river bank upstream from Ross which is part of the Wye Valley Walk. This passes under Bridstow Bridge and continues on to **Foy Footbridge (56)**, 4.5km upstream, and in the opposite direction to Wilton Bridge, 1.4km downstream. (ACRU, DLI, HWHP)

BRIDSTOW   The bridge built in 1960 for the Ross bypass with two main cantilevered spans of pre-stressed concrete connected by a short suspended span, though the latter cannot be distinguished in the photograph.

59 ROSS-ON-WYE, Wilton Bridge   B4260 connecting the A40 trunk road with Ross

Map 4; 162; 1064; SO 590 242

UNTIL RECENTLY, this noble old bridge had been a vital link for nearly four centuries connecting Hereford and South Wales with Ross, Gloucester and London, and for many years carried the A40 on its way through the centre of Ross. Dating from about 1600, it was built as a toll bridge under an Act of Parliament of 1579, replacing a ferry. It has six semicircular ribbed arches built of red sandstone with massive piers and angled cutwaters. The end arch on the left bank is for floodwater and joins a causeway across the flood plain to Ross. The arches are bevelled and the voussoir joints are joggled, and the tops of the cutwaters are sloped up to parapet level to create large half-hexagon refuges. The total length of the bridge is 87m and its present width 7.6m.

During the Civil War, one of its arches on the Hereford side was blown up; and it was badly damaged in the great flood of 1795 which destroyed the bridges at **Glasbury (37)**, **Hay (38)** and **Whitney (39)**. A climax came in 1914 when the bridge had deteriorated so badly that the river could be seen through cracks in the roadway. As a result, the arches were strengthened with reinforced concrete hidden in the backfill behind the masonry. In 1939 the bridge was widened as a wartime measure by laying rolled-steel joists across the tops of the upstream cutwaters, thus increasing the width from an original 5.5m to the present 7.6m. In 1960 the new Ross bypass was opened as a continuation of the M50, crossing **Bridstow Bridge (58)** and connecting with the A40 at Wilton; and in 1985 it was connected with a new relief road which enabled the A40 to be diverted from Wilton Bridge to a route via the bypass. As a result, improvements were made in 1993 to the temporary work of 1939. So the bridge lost its trunk road status and lapsed into honourable semi-retirement carrying local traffic to and from Ross.

An unusual feature is the sundial which stands in the centre refuge on the downstream side. It was erected in 1718 in the centre refuge on the upstream side, and moved to its present position after the widening in 1939. It has four vertical dials which are oriented correctly to face the four cardinal points, but skew with the bridge. Because of the erosion of the stone faces it is not easy to read. However, test readings made on the dial on different occasions, and after applying the necessary corrections for longitude and equation of time, suggest that the dial is about 10-12 minutes 'slow' against GMT. Even so, it remains an attractive embellishment to the bridge.

(ACRU, HH4, RCHM1)

WILTON   This famous bridge, dating from 1597, is known for its distinctive sundial, added in 1718, with four vertical faces.

The south dial is registering approximately 8.50am at 10.00 BST on 8 September 1994 which, after corrections, represents about 10.10 BST.

60 KERNE BRIDGE, road   B4229 connecting B4228, Ross to Forest of Dean, with Goodrich and A40 to Monmouth

Map 4; 162; 1087/OL14; SO 581 192

KERNE BRIDGE, with its five graduated arches in different coloured sandstones - reds, greys and greens - and discreetly embellished cutwaters, has a claim to be the most beautiful bridge over the River Wye. Built in 1828 by B.D. Jones, according to a plaque set in the parapet, it is 65.1m long.

The ancient road between Ross and Monmouth, dating at least from Roman times, crossed the Wye immediately below Goodrich Castle at the spot still known as Goodrich Boat. In fact the castle was built here in the 13th century to guard the river and its crossing. In 1749 the route from Ross to the Forest of Dean along the south side of the Wye valley was turnpiked as far as Kerne (or 'Quern'), but it was not until the bridge was built 700m downstream from Goodrich Boat that the ancient road began to lose its importance. It was just at this time that the first road was built through the lower Wye Valley between old **Monmouth Wye Bridge (65)** and Chepstow (see **Bigsweir Bridge (69)**), and the construction of Kerne Bridge added to the improved communications between agricultural Herefordshire and the then industrial Forest of Dean. Built as a toll bridge, it was transferred to Herefordshire County Council in 1947 and the tolls abolished in September 1948. This was the latest of the many Wye toll bridges to have been taken over by the respective local councils, leaving **Whitney Toll Bridge (40)** as the only one on the river today for which payment is required, and only for wheeled vehicles. Overlooked by the massive ruins of Goodrich Castle on its rocky height, the bridge is located where the Wye leaves the open Herefordshire plain and enters the wooded gorges of the Forest of Dean plateau, one of the most attractive stretches of this beautiful river.

The lower photograph, taken in about 1906 from the left bank, shows the toll gate and adjoining toll house. The latter, since demolished, obscures the view of Goodrich Castle on the hill beyond. The masonry on the extreme right is the parapet of the bridge inserted in the approach embankment in about 1870 to enable the newly created Ross and Monmouth railway to pass underneath. Kerne Bridge station was situated off to the left of the picture. The station building is still in existence.
(EJ, HH3, HWHP, KK2)

KERNE BRIDGE, road   One of the most beautiful bridges on the river. Built in 1828, it has five graduated semicircular arches.

View from the left bank showing the toll gate and toll house before the tolls were abolished in 1948.

Neil Parkhouse Collection

61 KERNE BRIDGE, rail   Site of bridge on the former
Ross and Monmouth Railway

Map 4; 162; 1087/OL14; SO 582 187

THE RAILWAY connecting Ross-on-Wye with Monmouth was opened as far as Mayhill, Monmouth in 1873, and finally completed to Monmouth, Troy in 1874 (see **Monmouth, Troy (R&MR) (66)**). It was worked by the Great Western Railway but remained nominally independent until the grouping of 1922. The line closely followed the river for most of the way, and the first station after leaving Ross, except for a halt at Walford, was at the village of Kerne Bridge - originally known as 'the Quern' but later named after the road bridge **(60)** built in 1828. The station was located close to the road bridge on the left bank, though the village is 500m farther on, which is where the railway bridge crossed the river. It was a single-track skew bridge of plate-girder construction supported on cylindrical iron columns and masonry abutments, and aligned at an acute angle with the river. It was built by Edward Finch of Chepstow, formerly of Liverpool (see **Chepstow Railway Bridge (76)**). There were four main spans, each 22.8m long, and four shorter ones, two at each end, and each 10.4m long, totalling 133m in all. Below the bridge, the river follows a tight meander for some 5km almost enclosing a spur of a hill in the parish of Welsh Bicknor; but the railway took a short cut through a curved tunnel 526m long under the spur, and known variously as Lydbrook or Coppet Hill tunnel, to emerge at the end of **Lydbrook Junction Bridge (62)**. The line was closed to passenger traffic in 1959, but remained open for goods traffic between Ross and Lydbrook Junction until 1964, after which the bridge was demolished, only the abutments and approach embankments remaining.

A recreation park and picnic area in the village of Kerne Bridge now surround the left bank abutment and its approach embankment, which, although rather overgrown, can be examined in comfort. There is a stout fence round the top of the abutment to protect the short-sighted. The Wye Valley Walk closely follows the right bank between the road bridge and Lydbrook Junction railway bridge, and a good view of the left bank abutment and its embankment can be seen across the river. The walk passes close to the remains of the smaller abutment on the right bank.

The upper photograph viewed from the right bank shows the left bank abutment in the picnic park, while the lower one, taken before the line was closed, was taken from a point on the hillside, looking in a similar direction. (HH3, MCG)

KERNE BRIDGE, rail   The bridge site seen from the right bank looking towards the opposite abutment in the picnic park.

714 Bridge over River Wye at Kerne Bridge N' Ross.

The bridge in about 1909, seen from high above the right bank.   *David Postle Collection*

62 LYDBROOK JUNCTION   Former Ross and Monmouth Railway; now a footbridge

Map 4; 162; 1087/OL14; SO 587 177

THIS BRIDGE is the next downstream from **Kerne Bridge, rail (61)**, and was likewise built for the Ross and Monmouth Railway, worked by the Great Western Railway, and opened as far as Mayhill, Monmouth in 1873. It is a multi-spanned plate-girder bridge, very similar in construction to Kerne Bridge, except that it has one large span and seven shorter ones instead of four of each. The other difference is that whereas Kerne Bridge was demolished after the closure of the line in 1964, Lydbrook Junction Bridge is still standing, though reduced in status to a public footbridge. The large span is supported on two pairs of massive iron cylinders, and the shorter ones, three at the right bank end of the main span and four at the other end, are supported on pairs of slender double columns, all braced with cross-stays. The large span is 22.8m long and the shorter ones each 10.4m, making a total length of 95m. After passing through Lydbrook tunnel under a spur of Coppet Hill on its way from Kerne Bridge, the line emerged some 100m before reaching the left bank abutment, and after crossing the bridge it entered Lydbrook Junction Station. Here, in 1874, it was joined by the Severn and Wye Railway, thus providing a connection with the rail network serving the Forest of Dean coal mines. The Severn and Wye Railway, before reaching the junction, passed through the centre of Lower Lydbrook over a high multi-spanned bridge known as Lydbrook Viaduct, now demolished, but not to be confused with Lydbrook Junction Bridge. Lydbrook Junction Station has also been demolished and a cardboard packaging factory now occupies the site.

The upper photograph, taken from the right bank, shows its present use as a footbridge. The footway is on the downstream side which, as the lower photograph shows, was formerly the position of the single rail track. In the lower photograph, taken in 1965 shortly before the line was closed, the train is about to enter Lydbrook tunnel on its way to Kerne Bridge and Ross-on-Wye.

There are rights of way along both banks of the river: upstream for 4.6km to Kerne Bridge, rail, and downstream for 5.5km to **Huntsham Bridge (63)**. The Wye Valley Walk follows the former along the right bank and the latter along the left bank, crossing the river at Lydbrook Junction.

(MCG)

LYDBROOK JUNCTION   View from the right bank along the line of the bridge showing its present use as a footbridge.

View in 1965 looking downstream shortly before the line was closed. The train has just left Lydbrook Junction station.

B J Ashworth

63 HUNTSHAM   Minor road connecting B4229 from Goodrich with Symonds Yat East

Map 4; 162; 1087/OL14; SO 567 181

HUNTSHAM BRIDGE, with its narrow roadway, must be familiar to many motorists who visit the popular gorge of Symonds Yat, 3km downstream, as it is the nearest river crossing by road, and leads to the well-known viewpoint at Symonds Yat Rock.

Built in 1982, it is a gently arched continuous truss bridge in three spans supported on four wide cylindrical wrought-iron piers. The spans rest on cross-trusses with splayed iron lattice-work brackets at the top of the piers. The bridge was designed at County Hall, Worcester, and built by RDL Contracting Limited, its total length being 81.6m and its width 3.6m.

It is an almost exact replica of the one which it replaced, and which was built almost a century earlier in 1885, designed by Maynard & Cooke of Westminster. So many elegant 19th century bridges have been replaced by stark concrete beams (**Brynwern (30)** and **Erwood (33)** for example), functional and economical though they may be, that it is pleasing to find this preservation of a design from the past. The earlier bridge replaced two ferries, one for pedestrians and the other for vehicles and merchandise.

The most obvious difference between the two bridges is that the old one had a distinct hump whereas the new bridge allows the driver to see that the road is clear before he starts to cross it. Less obvious is the construction of the trusses. The old bridge was assembled from fabricated sections of wrought iron riveted together, whereas the new bridge is constructed from welded mild-steel hollow tubes of rectangular section. Only the stout cylindrical wrought-iron piers of the old bridge remain.

On the top of each of the piers is a solid coat of arms painted in colour. All the arms are the same, and in non-heraldic language they comprise a shield of blue and red divided down the middle with three white lions on their hind legs; and above the shield is a boy's head with a snake round his neck. The motto is 'Dew (Duw) A Digon', Welsh for 'God is Sufficient', and the arms are those of the celebrated Vaughan Family of Courtfield, whose seat is in Welsh Bicknor on the top of the hill in the bend of the river two miles to the east of the bridge. The Vaughans were a leading Roman Catholic family whose most famous member was Henry Vaughan who became Cardinal Archbishop of Westminster. In 1880 he succeeded to the title of the Courtfield estate, but renounced it in favour of his younger brother Francis Baynham Vaughan, during whose tenure the first Huntsham bridge was built.

(AHL, BGA, BLG, DNB, HWHP, JBG2)

HUNTSHAM   A truss-girder road bridge built in 1982 to replace the one shown below. It is similar but with a much reduced hump.

Built in 1855 with truss girders, it had a marked hump. The two bridges seem to be almost identical but see text.

J Groucott

64 BIBLINS Recreational footpath in the Forest of Dean

Maps 4/5; 162; 1087/OL14; SO 549 144

THE BRIDGE is situated in an area of the Forest of Dean known as Highmeadow which extends on either side of the river, and its unusual construction must be familiar to the countless numbers of walkers and canoeists enjoying the recreational facilities of the Forest. It was designed by Col. Packard, Chief Engineer, and built in 1957 in the workshops of the Forestry Commission (now Forest Enterprise) using as much timber as possible in its construction.

It is a suspension bridge, and each of its towers consists of two massive A-frames braced together, with an additional ground brace on each side making six legs in all. The towers are 6m high and the deck is suspended from a pair of steel wire-rope cables run over the top of the A-frames and anchored in concrete at either end of the bridge. The suspenders are of wood, all the same length, strapped to the cables and connected at the bottom to wooden transoms which in turn support wooden runners along the length of the bridge. The deck and parapets are made from sheets of welded steel mesh tightly lashed together and hooked over the main cables, and are an essential structural element of the bridge. Two shorter cables at each end take the strain of the deck mesh as a walking surface. The length of the span between towers is 58m, and the cables have a dip of 2m at the centre. Since the walkway is parallel with the cables and only 1.2m below them, substantial wooden stairways have been built at each end. Windbrace cables are extended at intervals from the bridge to the river banks to control swaying.

Shortly before the First World War logging was started in Lords Wood on the right bank of the river. In order to transport the logs to the left bank, where there was a sawmill and a siding on the former Ross and Monmouth Railway, a cable transporter with a cradle for the logs was constructed across the river. It continued in use until at least 1929 and is shown in the lower photograph taken from the right bank.

In 1919 the Forestry Commission was established to rehabilitate the Nation's timber reserves, and the Forest and Highmeadow Woods were transferred to the Commission. In 1938 the Forest was designated a National Forest Park and its committee recommended that it should be developed for amenity and recreational use, and after the Second World War the recommendations were implemented to include camping, picnic sites, canoeing, waymarked walks etc, and it was under this policy that the present bridge was built.

There are public rights of way along both banks of the river and the Wye Valley Walk crosses the bridge from the right bank to the left on its way upstream where it then follows the now-disused railway track.
(CEH, TL, JEE)

BIBLINS   A delightful suspension footbridge built in 1957 by the Forestry Commission, now Forest Enterprise.

A forerunner of the above was a transporter bridge carrying logs suspended from pulleys running on two cables.

Forest Enterprise

65 MONMOUTH, Wye Bridge   A466 through the Lower
Wye Valley to Chepstow and A4136 to the Forest of Dean

Map 5; 162; 1087/OL14; SO 511 127

THIS IS A HANDSOME BRIDGE of five gently curved segmental arches supported on massive masonry piers. The arches are of variegated red sandstone with corbel courses supporting the stone parapets. This visible part of the bridge dates from 1879 when it was widened on both sides. The total span is 71m and the present width between parapets is about 9m. Underneath the present arches, the original ones can be seen. These are semicircular with large cutwaters, angled both upstream and downstream, and which were evidently adapted to support the new arches when the bridge was widened. The spacing of the arches and the exceptional size of the cutwaters are similar to those at **Wilton Bridge, Ross (59)**. The date of the original bridge, according to an inscription said at one time to have been displayed on one of the piers, is 1615, and Wilton Bridge was completed in 1600, so the two are nearly contemporary. The lower illustration is from a watercolour by Mary Bagnall-Oakley and shows the bridge shortly before it was widened. The semicircular arches and the original cutwaters extending up to the parapet can be seen clearly. There was also a bridge across the Wye in the 13th Century, but it may not have been exactly at the same site.

During the Civil War, Monmouth was under the lordship of the Earl of Worcester and was nominally Royalist, but the townsfolk seem to have been indifferent to either cause. The town changed hands several times but neither the Wye Bridge nor the neighbouring Monnow Bridge suffered damage, unlike those at **Hereford (47)** and **Wilton (59)**. Before **Bigsweir Bridge (69)** was completed in 1828, carrying the first road between Monmouth and Chepstow, there were no other bridges between the two towns, and in the 18th century the lower Wye had become a commercial highway supporting trade between Monmouth and Bristol and beyond. Navigation was possible up to Hereford, but the many shallows farther upstream made travel beyond Monmouth less reliable. Brockweir, a short distance upstream from Tintern, was the navigation centre of the river, and shallow draught barges and trows (which had a mast and sail) were towed upstream by teams of bow hauliers.

The Wye Valley Walk follows the right bank closely for 6.3km from **Biblins Bridge (64)** to Monmouth. Here it crosses the bridge and continues downstream through the playing fields of Monmouth School and under the former railway bridges, **Troy (66)** and **(67)**, for 4.4km to Redbrook Bridge **(68)**, where it crosses the river again to the right bank.

(EJ, KK1, KK2)

WYE BRIDGE   Showing the semicircular arches of 1617 partly hidden by the segmental ones of the 1879 widening.

The bridge as seen in a watercolour by Mary Bagnall-Oakley shortly before it was widened.

Monmouth Museum

66 MONMOUTH, Troy (R&MR)   Former Ross and Monmouth Railway

Map 5; 162; 1087/OL14; SO 513 121

THE ROSS AND MONMOUTH RAILWAY was opened in 1873 between Ross-on-Wye and Mayhill, on the opposite side of the river from Monmouth; but it was not until the bridge was completed in 1874 that it could reach Troy Station, where it joined the Great Western Railway line between Pontypool and Wyesham, not far from Mayhill but crossing the river by its own bridge (see **Monmouth Troy (WVR) Bridge (67)**). The Ross and Monmouth Railway was worked from the beginning by the Great Western Railway, but the line between Troy and Lydbrook Junction was closed in 1959 (see **Kerne Bridge, rail (61)**). Fortunately the bridge still stands. It was built by Edward Finch of Chepstow (see **Chepstow Railway Bridge (76)**) and is an excellent example of a truss-girder bridge with three spans, the main central one having a curved top chord, and the shorter ones at each end with parallel chords, all supported on cylindrical iron piers. The main span is 46m long and each of the shorter ones 18m.

The Wye Valley Walk follows closely the left bank between **Redbrook Bridge (68)** and **Monmouth Wye Bridge (65)**, passing under the bridge and round the edge of the Monmouth School playing fields. There is no right of way across the bridge, but the former track bed of the railway is commonly used by pedestrians, though there is no walkway over the corrugations of the steel deck. The confluence of the River Monnow with the Wye can be seen some 150m upstream from the bridge.

(BMH, MCG)

TROY BRIDGE (R&MR)   A 3-span truss-girder bridge, the centre span with an arched top chord. It is still used by pedestrians.

The bridge under construction in 1873, looking downstream.   *Monmouth Museum*

67 MONMOUTH, Troy (WVR)   Partly demolished railway bridge, former Wye Valley Railway

Map 5; 162; 1087/OL14; SO 514 120

THIS, ANOTHER BRIDGE AT TROY STATION and 200m downstream from **Troy Bridge (R&MR) (66)**, is remarkable for its magnificent masonry 20-arch approach viaduct. It is still a prominent feature of the Wye Valley below Monmouth, though the span over the river has been dismantled.

The bridge was planned for the Coleford, Monmouth, Usk and Pontypool Railway which was intended to connect the Forest of Dean with South Wales by joining the Newport, Abergavenny and Hereford Railway at Pontypool. The line was authorized in 1853 and reached Monmouth from Pontypool in 1857 where it terminated for nearly four years. However, in 1861 the bridge was built, and the line extended for a further 1km across the river to Wyesham where it terminated again. Meantime, the line had been leased to the West Midland Railway, an amalgamation of the lines between Oxford and Newport, including the Newport, Abergavenny and Hereford Railway, and in 1865 the West Midland Railway was absorbed in turn by the Great Western Railway, but neither of the new operators was interested in extending it into the Forest of Dean. Furthermore, the short Wyesham extension was used only for freight traffic, so the splendid and costly bridge must have been something of a white elephant. It was not until 1876 that the Wye Valley Railway completed its line from the South Wales Railway near Chepstow to Wyesham, enabling traffic to run between Chepstow and Monmouth, with intermediate stations along the lower Wye Valley, that the bridge came into its own. The South Wales Railway became part of the Great Western system in 1905. (A connection was eventually made with the Forest of Dean in 1883 when the independent Coleford Railway was constructed from Wyesham Junction to Coleford, but the line was closed in 1916.)

The river crossing was by a single lattice-girder deck bridge, 46m long, its right bank abutment forming the end of the masonry viaduct, 183m long, and the left bank abutment adjoining a two-arched bridge about 20m long. The iron span was removed after the line was finally closed in 1964.

The Wye Valley Walk follows the left bank between **Redbrook Bridge (68)** and **Monmouth, Wye Bridge (65)**, passing through an abutment arch of Troy Bridge (WVR) and also under Troy Bridge (R&MR). The latter can be crossed, though it is not a right of way, and there is a well marked anglers' path which follows the right bank downstream to the base of the viaduct. The deck along the top of the viaduct is closed by a locked gate.

(BMH, CA, JP)

TROY BRIDGE (WVR)   Part of the 20-arch viaduct approach to the lattice-girder span built in 1861, looking upstream.

A view of the lattice-girder span before it was removed after the line was closed in 1964. *Monmouth Museum*

68 REDBROOK   Former Wye Valley Railway, now a footpath

Map 5; 162; OL14; SO 536 098

THE WYE VALLEY RAILWAY was built to connect Monmouth with Chepstow and was opened in 1876, joining the West Midland Railway at Wyesham and the South Wales Railway at Wye Valley Junction. The trains crossed the river by four bridges: **Monmouth Troy (WVR) (67)**, **Redbrook (68)**, **Tintern (69)** and **Chepstow, rail (76)**. Of these, only Redbrook and Tintern were built by the Wye Valley Railway though ultimately they all became part of the Great Western Railway.

On its way downstream from Wyesham, the line crossed the river from the left bank to the right at Redbrook, the location of an important tinplate works which eventually closed in 1961. The bridge is a plate-girder structure with five spans supported on four pairs of cylindrical iron columns filled with concrete. It is built on the skew with a gentle curve, and has an overall length of about 90m. A ferry originally occupied the site as is testified by the name of the Boat Inn on the right bank opposite the village. There was a station near each end of the bridge: Redbrook-on-Wye on the left bank (the site is now occupied by a Little Chef restaurant) and Penallt Halt on the right.

In 1955, a footway with precast-concrete decking was attached to the outside of the upstream girders, and after closure of the line in 1964, the ownership of the bridge was transferred to the counties on either side of the river, now Gwent and Gloucestershire. The car park for the Boat Inn is on the left bank in Redbrook, so the bridge is still important for customers of the inn as well as for walkers following the Wye Valley Walk which crosses the river at this point.

The upper photograph shows the bridge today, seen from Redbrook on the left bank, and looking much as it would have done when first built. The lower photograph taken from the right bank shows the walkway outside the main upstream girder, and the position of the rail track now removed, as well as the skew and curvature of this unusual bridge.

(BMH, BRIS, KK2)

REDBROOK   A truss-girder skew bridge built for the WVR in 1876. The line was closed in 1964 but the bridge is still used by walkers.

View along the bridge from the right bank showing the walkway outside the main girder and the curvature of the bridge.

69 BIGSWEIR BRIDGE A466 between Monmouth and Chepstow

Map 5; 162; OL14; SO 538 051

THE RIVER FLOWS SOUTHWARD from Monmouth to Chepstow through the scenic gorge of the Lower Wye Valley bordering the west side of the Forest of Dean plateau. Today, it is difficult to believe that this was once an area of industrial activity. The Romans mined coal and iron in the Forest of Dean using the abundant timber for charcoal to smelt the iron ore, and by the 18th century the mining industry was fully developed. The many streams draining into the river from both banks were used to supply water-powered forges, blast furnaces and mills for the manufacture of tin-plate, wire and paper, as well as grinding corn. There was copper smelting at Redbrook, though the ore was shipped from Cornwall. In fact the river supplied all transport needs into and out of Chepstow and as far north as Hereford. Even the tourists, following Gilpin's cult of the Picturesque, which he advocated in his *Observations on the River Wye* in 1782, were taken by rowing boat from Ross to Tintern and back. However, in 1824 a toll road was authorised and was opened four years later. It led from **Monmouth Wye Bridge (65)** along the left bank (in Gloucestershire) to the upper tidal limit half way to Chepstow near Bigsweir House where it crossed the river to the opposite bank (then in Monmouthshire but now in Gwent).

Bigsweir Bridge is a fine example of early 19th century bridge building. It has a single flat arch of 50m span with four ribs of cast-iron segments and a slightly humped deck, and the spandrels have N-pattern bracing, all in cast iron. The bridge was designed by Charles Hollis of London, and the components were cast at Merthyr Tydfil. In the mid-19th century two masonry flood arches were added at each end, and recently the stonework has been substantially repaired, but otherwise the bridge stands today as built. Its total length is 98m but it is only 3.6m wide. The bridge continues to carry the busy traffic, including a high proportion of tourists, across the river. The old toll house stands empty at the Gwent end of the bridge.

A low-level branch of Offa's Dyke Path follows the left bank of the river between Brockweir and Bigsweir Bridge where it rejoins the main path, and the Wye Valley Walk follows the high ground along the west side some distance from the river; but the bridge provides a means of interchange between the two long distance paths by following the track of the old Wye Valley Railway along the right bank (not a right of way), which joins the Wye Valley Walk a mile farther upstream at Whitebrook.

(FDWV, KK2, SDC, WJS)

BIGSWEIR   An elegant cast-iron bridge with a single gentle arch built as a toll bridge in 1828, looking upstream towards Monmouth.

70 BROCKWEIR   Minor road connecting Brockweir and the western Forest of Dean with A466

Map 5; 162; OL14; SO 539 011

THE TOLL ROAD between Monmouth and Chepstow which opened up the lower Wye Valley (now A466), and which crosses the River at **Bigsweir Bridge (69)**, was opened in 1828, but Brockweir did not have its bridge until 1906. The village was an important port as well as a ship and boat building centre, mostly of vessels up to 100 tons and especially the man-hauled Wye barges and trows, which had a mast and sail, but in the 1820s and until the coming of the railway, barques and brigantines over 500 tons were being built. The bridge, which replaced a ferry, has three lattice-girder spans supported on two pairs of cylindrical columns and masonry abutments. It was constructed in Chepstow by Edward Finch & Company and the spans were floated up the river on barges.

   The Wye Valley Walk follows the right bank upstream from Tintern to the end of Brockweir Bridge from where it turns off to climb over the hills to Whitebrook; on the other hand, one of the alternative routes of Offa's Dyke Path diverges from the main route which follows the high ground from Chepstow, and descends to the river at Brockweir to follow the left bank upstream to Bigsweir Bridge. Neither crosses the bridge; but see **Hay-on-Wye (38)** where these two long distance paths meet again and share the bridge before separating on the other side to follow their differing routes.

(AH, KK2)

BROCKWEIR A 3-span lattice-girder bridge built in 1906 to connect Brockweir with the Monmouth to Chepstow road.

View of Brockweir, an important navigation and boat building town, before the bridge was built.

Monmouth Museum

71 TINTERN, Station   Site of demolished bridge,
Wye Valley Railway

Map 5; 162; OL14; SO 535 004

THE RAILWAY, following the right bank of the river from **Redbrook Bridge (68)**, and on approaching Tintern, reached a right hand bend, the start of the 'Tintern Loop'. Instead of following the loop it crossed the river by Tintern Bridge and thence by a tunnel through the neck of the loop and continued its way towards Chepstow along the left bank of the river, thus avoiding Tintern and its famous Abbey ruins. The bridge consisted of a continuous lattice girder 54m long supported on two pairs of cylindrical iron columns filled with concrete and masonry abutments, and the line entered the tunnel almost immediately after crossing the bridge. A station was built near the bridge and was named 'Tintern for Brockweir' since it lay between the two villages. However, the station was a mile away from the centre of Tintern but only half that distance from Brockweir, which did not please the inhabitants of Tintern.

The ironwork of the bridge was removed in 1964-5 after the line was closed, but the station and its yard have been adapted as a picnic park with a railway motif which includes the course of the old railway as far as the right bank abutment of the bridge. The Wye Valley Walk, after passing through Tintern and following round the loop, reaches the station and then follows the course of the old railway to Brockweir Bridge, thereafter traversing the high ground to the west of the river to Whitebrook and so along the river bank again to Redbrook Bridge.

The upper photograph, looking upstream, at this point eastward, shows the site of the bridge where it crossed the river at the start of the Tintern Loop. Tintern Station was beyond the left edge and the entrance to the tunnel to the right of the downstream abutment but not visible here. The lower photograph shows much the same view but from a greater distance and includes the whole loop. A white streak by the river to the right of the neck of the loop shows where the line emerged from the tunnel. The **Wireworks Bridge (72)** is on the right of the photograph and the Wireworks branch (now a right of way) follows the left bank of the river to meet the main line near the tunnel exit. The ruins of Tintern Abbey can be seen in the distance.
(BMH)

TINTERN   Site of a lattice-girder bridge of the WVR where the river makes a sharp bend towards Tintern.

Distant view of Tintern Loop. The bridge is on the left and the **Wireworks Bridge (72)** is on the right.

Ian Pope Collection

72 TINTERN, Wireworks   Former Wye Valley Railway
branch line; now public access to woods on the left bank

Map 5; 162; OL14; S 0530 003

THIS BRIDGE, familiar to all who pass through Tintern, has three truss-girder spans with masonry piers and abutments, the latter pierced with flood arches. The length between abutments is 65m and it was constructed by the Isca Foundry Company of Newport to the design of S.H. Yockney of Westminster. The bridge is sited just above the mouth of the Angidy River, the lowest of the many tributaries in the lower Wye Valley with water mills which for centuries had supplied power for a variety of industries. In 1821 there were no less than twenty water wheels on the Angidy alone.

In 1566 the Government wished to establish wire making in England and selected the Angidy for the first works. The project was a success and during the succeeding years there were at least eight separate sites on the river which at one time or another were involved in some aspect of wire making, and there were other industries as well. The land on which the works were sited belonged to the Dukes of Beaufort, and when it was learned in about 1872 that the projected Wye Valley Railway would bypass Tintern (see **Tintern (71)**), the then duke prevailed on the railway company to build a branch line to reach the lower of the two wireworks then operating. The company would build the line and the bridge across the Wye, and would add a siding at the point of connection with the main line to be known as Wireworks Junction. It would also provide rolling stock, but the wireworks lessees would have to find the locomotive and operate the branch line. However, during the 19th century wireworking had been in decline, and by 1875 when the line had been completed, the wireworks company had gone out of business. It was not until the early 1880s that it was restarted and the line came into use, but by 1901 wireworking had ceased altogether. The line was then used as a horse-drawn tramway by the operator of a sawmill and joinery works until the mid 1930s when the track had deteriorated beyond economic repair, and in 1941 the rails were lifted and sold for the war effort.

The bridge is now owned by the respective county councils of Gwent and Gloucestershire on either side of the river, and provides public access to the woods on the Gloucestershire side. A walk follows the route of the old Wye Valley Railway southward for 3km, another leads to Brockweir, 1.6km distant, and there are two which climb to the top of the hill - about 175m in elevation above the river - to join Offa's Dyke Path.

(BMH, SDC)

WIREWORKS BRIDGE   Built for a private branch line serving the wireworks on the Angidy river, now a public right of way.

73 CHEPSTOW, Roman bridge   Presumed site

Map 5; 162; OL14/1131; ST 531 948

THE ROMANS BUILT A ROAD to what is now South Wales from Weston-under-Penyard (Ariconium), probably with a branch from Gloucester (Glevum), leading to Caerwent (Venta) and Caerleon (Isca) and crossing the Wye close to present day Chepstow. Margary, in his authoritative account of Roman roads in Britain, places the crossing at Castleford, an area between Tutshill and the river; and Waters, in his study of Chepstow bridges, describes it as 'west of Tutshill and north-east of St Kingsmark'. More precisely, the Ordnance Survey 1:2500 map in the old County Series shows a Roman bridge in line with a hollow in the cliffs in Alcove Wood on the right bank. Below the hollow, the end of the river at high tide is shown as an irregular line with two or three small embayments. However, the bridge site is not shown on the current survey at the same scale, but it does show that the parish boundary between Chepstow and St Arvans follows the line of the hollow; and old parish boundaries frequently follow the course of Roman roads - as for instance the boundary between Madley and Eaton Bishop on the right bank at the site of **Kenchester Roman Bridge (44)**.

It is surprising that the Romans should have chosen to cross the river where it was bordered by high cliffs, but at least this 'dingle', as Bradney describes the hollow in his *History of Monmouthshire*, provides the only feasible way up, and helps to establish the location of the bridge at this point. Margary and Brigadier Hamilton-Baillie, the latter in his study of Roman roads near Chepstow, both argue for a branch road leading from some point beyond the end of the bridge to Monmouth, but they differ as to where that point is. Hamilton-Baillie describes a terraced roadway branching off at the end of the bridge and climbing up the hillside towards Chepstow, but he gives no evidence that it is of Roman origin; while Margary places the junction near the present roundabout on the A446 at High Beach. On the other hand the Ordnance Survey on its map of Roman Britain shows no road at all between Chepstow and Monmouth.

Normally there is nothing of the bridge to be seen today, but from time to time in exceptionally low water some timbers have been reported in this locality. In 1911, excavations exposed what were believed to have been vertical posts of the Roman bridge. Oddly enough the excavations were made, not in connection with the Roman bridge, but in an attempt by an American researcher who hoped to recover manuscripts which would show that Bacon wrote Shakespeare's plays. In 1962, Waters visited the site and recovered some pieces of wood which have been lodged in the Chepstow museum, but they have not been age-tested to determine whether they could indeed be of Roman origin.

The bridge was probably located opposite the shadowed gap in the river bank in the right half of the photograph. The view is from the left bank which can be reached from a private farm track leading NNW from near the bottom of the Castleford Hill road (it is not a right of way). On the right bank the Wye Valley Walk follows the upper slopes of Alcove Wood and makes an inward bend where it crosses the dingle, but descent to the river is steep and heavily overgrown.

(AR, IDM, IW, JHB)

ROMAN BRIDGE   Probably located opposite the shadowed gap in the river bank in the right half of the photograph.

74 CHEPSTOW, old road bridge   Minor road between Chepstow and Tutshill

Map 5; 162; OL14/1131; ST 536 943

THIS ELEGANT BRIDGE of five graduated arches was opened in 1816. The arches are of cast iron with spandrel fillings of a radiating grid pattern supported on masonry piers. John Rennie, the famous bridge builder of the day, was invited to submit a design, but evidently his estimated cost was too high and the contract was given to Hazeldine, Rastrick & Brodie of Bridgnorth. John Rastrick was the designer of the bridge, though he may have been influenced by Rennie. In 1889, Edward Finch & Co of Chepstow strengthened the bridge by adding steel ribs to the original cast iron, and in 1914 the foundations were strengthened with concrete piling, and later with steel sheet piling. The central span measures 34m, the flanking spans each 21m and 10m, making a total of 95m. The width between parapets is 6m.

Until the **New Road Bridge (75)** was built in 1987, the old bridge carried all the A48 traffic coming into Chepstow from the east, a load far in excess of that contemplated by Rastrick; and since the width of the bridge necessitated one-way traffic with controlling lights, there was severe congestion. Now the bridge has been relegated to that of a minor road serving local traffic between Chepstow and Tutshill and villages to the north.

The first bridge, apart from the possible **Roman Bridge (73)** farther upstream, is recorded in the 13th century. It was built of wood and was frequently in ill repair. A new bridge was built in 1546, and Acts of 1575 and 1605-6 stipulated that the cost of repair should be shared between the counties on either side: Monmouthshire and Gloucestershire. In 1703, the bridge was described as being built mostly of wood bearing on stone platforms on the river bed and with a stone pier in the middle marking the boundary between the two counties. A drawing by Kip in 1705 shows such a bridge, and an engraving by William Byrne after Richard Hoare in William Coxe's *Historical Tour through Monmouthshire* of 1801, reproduced here, shows the piers on the Monmouthshire side to be of masonry but those on the Gloucestershire side to be of timber of 'Roman type so contrived to present only a narrow surface to the current of the river'. A print published by J. Deeley of London in 1812 appears to show all the piers built of masonry but protected with wood starlings. This is presumably the bridge which was damaged when a passing pleasure boat fouled the mooring rope of another tied to the bridge. Seven people were drowned and the bridge was damaged, leading to the decision to build the present iron bridge.

(AR, IW)

OLD ROAD BRIDGE   Built in 1816 with graduated segmental arches and decorative spandrels of cast iron.

The bridge of 1775 with both stone piers and wooden ones. From an engraving by W. Byrne in Coxe's *Historical Tour through Monmouthshire.*

75 CHEPSTOW, new road bridge   A48 between Gloucester and South Wales

Map 5; 162; OL14/1131; ST 539 941

FOR OVER A CENTURY AND A HALF, Rastrick's narrow cast-iron **Old Bridge (74)** carried all the road traffic into Chepstow from the east, and a relief road had been long overdue when the new bridge was built in 1987 providing a through road to the M4 motorway as well as access to Chepstow. The bridge is located immediately alongside Brunel's **Railway Bridge (76)** of 1852, and the problems associated with the site are the same as those which faced Brunel: a solid cliff of Carboniferous Limestone 36m high rising sheer from the water's edge on the left bank, and a flat of river clay and gravel some 180m wide and a little above high water level on the right bank. So as not to change the existing visual effect, it was decided that the new bridge should follow closely the profile of the adjacent railway bridge. (Brunel's famous tubular suspension span had been replaced in 1962 by truss girders placed below the railway track.) To accommodate the approach to the bridge on the left bank, the railway cutting was widened to the same depth so that the decks of the two bridges should be at the same level, about 27m above the water at lowest tide or 15m above the highest tide; and the cylindrical piers were of similar size and spacing to correspond with those of the earlier bridge. The result is that to the casual observer, whether looking upstream or downstream, the two bridges appear almost as one.

The main span over the river is 93m long, and consists of an open-topped steel box girder, while the four approach spans on the west side, totalling 200m, are of two continuous plate girders. The carriageway deck, 5.4m wide, is a continuous slab of concrete poured in place. The walkways and hard shoulders, one on each side, and the parapets are cantilevered out from the deck, and to enhance their appearance the angle between the vertical and horizontal faces is rounded, and the surface of the parapets has a ribbed finish. The cylindrical concrete piers, also with ribbed surfaces, rest on steel piles driven through the gravels to limestone bedrock some 15m below. The steelwork was put in place by 'launching': that is to say, it was first constructed on rollers set on top of the approach piers, and then winched across the river from the opposite bank.

The consulting engineers were Ove Arup & Partners and the consulting architects the Alex Gordon Partnership. The main contractor was A. Monk & Company, and the steel subcontractor Fairfield-Mabey Limited, whose works are situated nearby.

There is a pleasant riverside walk along the right bank of the river from the old bridge to the new, and it is the view from here that is seen in the photograph below. Comparison with this and the upper photograph on page 159 of the adjoining railway bridge (76) shows how closely the design of the new road bridge follows the profile of its older neighbour. In fact, the truss girder which appears to be suspended below the deck of the road bridge is that of the rebuilt railway bridge.
(GB)

NEW ROAD BRIDGE   Built in 1987 alongside the railway bridge (76), the main span is an open steel box girder, but the truss girder which appears to hang below it belongs to the railway bridge.

76 CHEPSTOW, Rail   Gloucester to South Wales Line

Map 5; 162; OL14/1131; ST 539 940

THE BRIDGE SEEN TODAY, with its distinctive set of truss girders slung below the main span, is a 1962 rebuild of I.K. Brunel's famous bridge of 1852. By 1851 the South Wales Railway had completed its broad-gauge line linking the Great Western Railway from Gloucester with Swansea, except for crossing the Wye at Chepstow. For this, Brunel designed an unusual bridge, typical of his inventiveness. He was faced with a sheer limestone cliff 36m high on the left bank and a level area of clay and gravel about 1.2m above high water on the right. The Admiralty insisted on 15m headroom above the highest known tide. On the right bank he used three approach spans of plate girders 30m long supported on hollow cast-iron cylinders sunk some 15m through the clay to bedrock. This was achieved by excavating the clay inside the cylinders by hand and applying heavy weights at the top. The work was carried out under compressed air to exclude water, a relatively new technique then. When the cylinders reached bedrock they were filled with concrete. The approach from the east was made through a cutting in the limestone leading directly to the main span across the river. For this span of 94m he suspended the track girders on diagonal bar chains from two gently arched wrought-iron tubes 2.7m in diameter, one above each track. These were supported at each end on masonry towers astride the track, 15m high, a structure so extraordinary it became one of the sights of Chepstow.

To build the Chepstow bridge Brunel engaged Edward Finch of Liverpool. After its completion Finch stayed on, and his business, located on the river bank by the bridge, developed into a major engineering enterprise, succeeded after the Second World War by Fairfield Shipbuilding & Engineering Company, and then by Fairfield-Mabey Limited.

When in 1962 British Rail found it necessary to replace Brunel's structure, it was Fairfield-Mabey who undertook the work. The four Warren truss girders were assembled on the right bank and winched across the river slung beneath the bridge. The girders are bolted with high strength friction-grip bolts which rely on the friction between the surfaces of the two adjoining sections rather than the sheer strength of the bolts. This was the first use of this type in England. When the girders were in place beneath the main span, Brunel's tubes and towers were dismantled.

The bridge can be reached from the riverside walk leading downstream from the old road bridge. It is possible to picks one's way under both the new bridge and the railway bridge to the almost deserted wharves beyond.
(AR, GB, LTCR)

RAILWAY BRIDGE Brunel's bridge of 1852 was rebuilt in 1962 with truss girders below the track instead of his suspension system.

The bridge as originally built showing the famous tube and bar chain suspension.

F Burtt Collection, National Railway Museum, York

77 CHEPSTOW, Severn Bridge (Wye section)   M4 between London and South Wales

Map 5; 162; 1131; ST 543 912

UNTIL THE BRIDGE was opened by Queen Elizabeth II in 1966 road traffic between southern England and South Wales had to cross the River Severn by ferry from Aust to Beachley or else go via Gloucester. The structure consists of four bridges end to end: a suspension bridge across the Severn between Aust and Beachley; a ten-span steel girder viaduct across the Beachley peninsula between the Severn and the Wye; a cable-stayed bridge across the Wye itself; and another steel viaduct of three spans to the higher ground at Chepstow. The whole length of the four bridges is about 3km. It is known as The Severn Bridge, but it is the Wye section, the last bridge across the river before it joins the Severn, which chiefly concerns us here.

The Severn section is a true suspension bridge with the deck girder suspended from parallel catenaries passing over wide towers astride the deck; whereas the Wye section is cable-stayed, which means that the cables from the towers are anchored directly to the deck girder. It has two slender towers on the centre line of the bridge, from which two pairs of cable stays are splayed lengthways either side of the tower. One pair is attached at the top of the tower and the other half way up and both are anchored to the deck along the centre line. The eight anchorage points are evenly spaced, including bases of the towers, in a symmetrical pattern. The deck girders are hollow steel boxes of flat rectangular cross-section to which are added similar boxes of triangular cross-section designed to present a streamlined profile against the force of the wind as well as acting as walkways on each side of the bridge. They were fabricated in Chepstow by Fairfield-Mabey Limited. The height of the towers is 38m above the deck and the span is 235m between towers or twice that amount for the total length of the cable-stayed structure.

As originally built, the towers were 30m high with only one pair of cable stays each, but by 1982 new design loadings for bridges had been introduced, and in view of the greatly increased traffic load, the Ministry of Transport decided to strengthen the whole structure. This involved extending the towers, removing the original stays and replacing them with the two sets of new ones. The work was carried out by Fairfield-Mabey without closing the bridge to traffic, a unique operation which needed a year to complete.

There is a cycle path and walkway along each side of the bridge from which details can be seen at close quarters, and for uninterrupted views at greater distances there are farm road exits from the Newhouse Farm Warehousing

Estate leading across the railway lines to the meadow flats by the river. There is no access from the Beachley Peninsula where the land is the property of the Ministry of Defence.
(AR, GB, WJS)

SEVERN BRIDGE, WYE SECTION   A cable-stayed bridge, each tower with two pairs of stays, looking south towards the Severn Estuary.

As originally built, the towers were shorter and there was only one pair of stays per tower.

Eric de Maré, *Bridges of Britain*, (B T Batsford Ltd)

SOURCES

ACRU	AA Cartographic Research Unit, personal communication
AH	Helme, Andrew. *Monmouth and the River Wye in Old Photographs*, (Alan Sutton, 1989)
AHL	Lamont, Arthur H. 'Fords and Ferries of the Wye' in *Transactions of the Woolhope Club*, 1922
AR	Rainsbury, Anne. *Chepstow and the River Wye in Old Photographs*, (Chepstow Museum, 1989)
BGA	*Burke's General Armoury*
BLc	Bryan Lawrence, Powys Library Service, personal communication
BLd	Bernard Lloyd, Rhayader, personal communication
BLG	*Burke's Landed Gentry*
BRIS	British Rail Infrastructure Services, Western Examination Section, Newport, Gwent.
BMH	Handley, Brian M. *The Wye Valley Railway*, (Oakwood Press, 1982)
BWM	B.W. Moorsom, personal communication
CA	Awdry, Christopher. *British Railway Companies*, (Patrick Stephens, 1990)
CC	Cook, R. A. and Clinker, C. R. *Early Railways between Abergavenny and Hereford*, (Railway and Canal Historical Society, c1984)
CEH	Hart, Cyril E. *Royal Forest*, (Clarendon Press, 1966)
CIA	Courtauld Institute of Art, Witt Library, personal communication
CJ	Judge, Colin. *The Elan Valley Railway*, (Oakwood Press, 1987)
CTG	*County Times and Gazette*, Newtown, 12 August 1994
CVL	Llewellyn, Sir Charles. 'The Old Wye Bridge at Newbridge-on-Wye' in *Transactions of the Radnor Society*, vol. 3, 1932
CW	Wood, C. *Dictionary of Victorian Painters*, (Antique Collectors' Club, 2nd Edition, 1978)
DAT	Revd David Tipper, Hereford, unpublished notes, 1988
DB	Bick, David. *The Old Metal Mines of Mid-Wales*, Parts 4/5, (The Pound House, new edn., 1990)
DD	Davies, Dewi. *Bridges of Breconshire*, (The author, 1991)
DEO	Owen, Rev. D.E. 'Notes on Antiquities in the Parish of Llanelwedd' in *Transactions of the Radnorshire Society*, vol. 18, 1948
DH	Hunter, David. *Walking Down the Wye*, (Cicerone Press, 1992)
DLI	D. L. Ings, Scott Wilson Kirkpatrick & Partners, personal communication
DNB	*Dictionary of National Biography*
DV	David Vaughan, personal communication
EGW	*Encyclopaedia of the Great Western Railway*, Patrick Stephens, 1993
EJ	Jervoise, E. *The Ancient Bridges of Wales and Western England*, (Architectural Press, 1936, reprinted EP Publishing, 1976)
ES	Edward Sayers, Severn Trent Water, personal communication
FBE1	Ellison, F.B. 'Whitney Bridge and Whitney Ferry' in *Transactions of the Woolhope Club*, 1935
FBE2	-- 'History of the Hay Railway' in *Transactions of the Newcomen Society*, vol.18, 1937-8

FDWV	*Guide to the Forest of Dean and Wye Valley*, (AA and Ordnance Survey, 1988)
GB	Geoffrey Booth, Fairfield-Mabey Limited, personal communication
GBJ	Gwyn Briwnant-Jones, personal communication
GD	George Day, Tysons Limited, personal communication
GHJ	Jack, G.H. 'Ancient Bridges in Herefordshire and their Preservation' in *Transactions of the Woolhope Club*, 1926
GHR	Howard Roberts, Rhayader Angling Society, personal communication
GWM	*Great Western Railway Magazine*, vol. 59, No.10, 1947
HCM	Moore, H.C. 'The Supposed Roman Bridge in the Grounds of the New Weir, Kenchester' in *Transactions of the Woolhope Club*, 1913
HH1	Hurley, Heather. 'River Crossing at Hoarwithy' in *Transactions of the Woolhope Club*, 1982
HH2	-- 'Foy Bridge, Herefordshire' in *Journal of the Wye Valley Countryside Service*, 1987
HH3	-- *The Old Roads of South Herefordshire*, (The Pound House, 1992)
HH4	-- *A History of the River Crossing at Wilton-on-Wye, Herefordshire*, (Ross-on-Wye Civic Society, 1993)
HJH	Hurley, H. & J. *The Wye Valley Walk*, (Thornhill Press, 1994)
HP	H.W. Paar, Chigwell, Essex, personal communication
HR	Harry Rice, Llanwrthwl, personal communication
HT	*History of Technology*, vol. 5, (Oxford, 1958)
HW	Williams, Herbert. *Stage Coaches in Wales*, (S. Williams, 1977)
HWHP	Hereford and Worcester CC, Dept. of Highways and Planning, personal communication
HWRO	Hereford and Worcester County Record Office, Hereford
IDM	Margary, Ivan D. *Roman Roads in Britain*, third edn. (John Baker, 1973)
IW	Waters, Ivor. *Chepstow Road Bridges*, (Moss Rose Press, reprint 1980)
IWM	Imperial War Museum, personal communication
JAC	Cash, J.A. *The River Wye*, (Chapman and Hall, 1952)
JBG1	Groucott, J.B. *Brynwern Bridge 1885*, (privately printed, 1978)
JBG2	Jim Groucott, Rhayader, personal communication
JEE	John Everard, Forest Enterprise, personal communication
JGW	Julian Gibson-Watt, Doldowlod, personal communication
JHB	Hamilton-Baillie, Brig. J. 'Roman Roads near Chepstow' in *Severn and Wye Review*, vol. 2, no.2, 1972/3
JM	Morris, Jacqueline, in Geoffrey L. Fairs, *A History of the Hay*, (Phillimore, 1972)
JP	Page, James. *Forgotten Railways*, vol. 8, *South Wales*, (David & Charles, 1988)
JW	Williams, Rev. J. *A General History of the County of Radnor*, E. Davies (ed.), (Brecknock, 1905)
KD	*Kilvert's Diary*, W. Plomer (ed.), vol. 3, (Jonathan Cape, 1940)
KK1	Kissack, Keith. *Monmouth, The Making of a County Town*, (Phillimore, 1975)
KK2	-- *The River Wye*, (Terence Dalton, 1978)

LGB	Booth, L.G. 'Timber Works' in A. Pugsley (ed.) *The Works of Isambard Kingdom Brunel*, (Inst. Civil Eng. London, Univ. of Bristol, 1976)
LTCR	Rolt, L.T.C. *Isambard Kingdom Brunel*, (Longmans, 1957)
MacD	MacDermot, E.T. *History of the Great Western Railway*, vol. 1, revised Clinker, (1964)
MCG	Glover, M and C. *The Ross and Monmouth Railway*, (Brewin Books, 1994)
NRH	N.R. Hope, Newbridge-on-Wye, personal communication
SOED	*Shorter Oxford English Dictionary*, 1936
PCA	Powys County Archives Office
PHD	Powys Highways Department, personal communication
PT	Peter Tomlinson, Mabey & Johnson Limited, personal communication
PW	Philip Wolfindon, British Steel Corporation, personal communication
RCHM	Royal Commission on Historical Monuments, England *Herefordshire*, vol. 1, South-West, (1931), vol. 2, East, (1932)
RCRM	Christiansen, Rex and R.W. Miller. *The Cambrian Railways*, vol. 1, (David & Charles, 1967)
RH	Haslam, Richard. *Powys*, (The Buildings of Wales), (Penguin, 1979)
RJ	Roy James, Welsh Water, Hereford, personal communication
RMRE	Museum of the Royal Monmouthshire Royal Engineers, Monmouth
RSa	Sale, Richard. *The Wye Valley*, (Wildwood House, 1984)
RSh	Shoesmith, Ron. *Hereford: History and Guide*, 1992
RTCE	Railtrack Civil Engineering Directorate, Swindon
RWK	Kidner, R. W. *The Mid-Wales Railway*, (Oakwood Press, 1990)
SBE	Simon Bennet-Evans, personal communication
SDC	Coates, S.D. *The Water Powered Industries of the Lower Wye Valley*, (Monmouth Borough Museum Service, 1992)
TL	Trevor Lewis, Coleford, personal communication
TRP	Perkins, T.R. 'Railways in the Wye Valley', parts 2 and 3, in *Railway Magazine*, November and December, 1938
WJS	Sivewright, W.J. (ed). *Civil Engineering Heritage, Wales and West ern England*, (Thomas Telford for the Institute of Civil Engineering, 1986)

SELECTED BIBLIOGRAPHY

Berridge, P.S.A	'Civil Engineering, Part 1: Roads, Bridges and Tunnels' in *A History of Technology*, Trevor I. Williams, (ed.) vol. 7, 876-899, (Oxford, 1978)
Gordon, J.E.	*Structures - Or Why Things Don't Fall Down*, (Penguin, 1978)
Upton, Neil	*An Illustrated History of Civil Engineering*, (Heinemann, 1975)
Wright, G.N.	*Bridges of Britain*, (Bradford Barton, 1973)

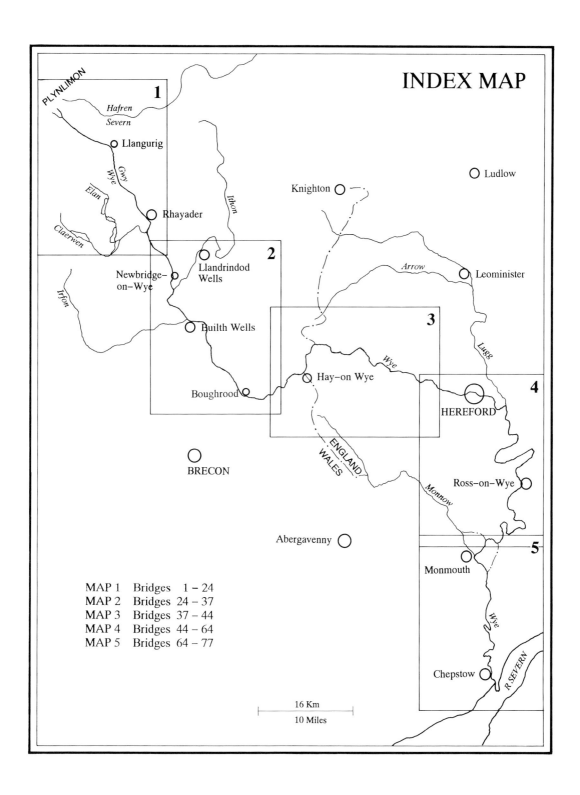

INDEX MAP

MAP 1   Bridges   1 – 24
MAP 2   Bridges 24 – 37
MAP 3   Bridges 37 – 44
MAP 4   Bridges 44 – 64
MAP 5   Bridges 64 – 77

16 Km
10 Miles

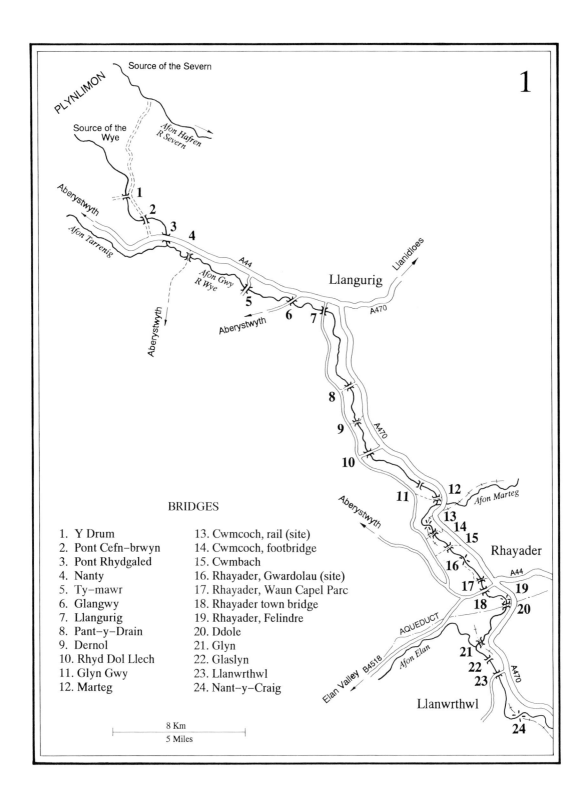

1

Source of the Severn

PLYNLIMON

Source of the Wye

Afon Hafren
R Severn

Aberystwyth

1

2

3 **4**

Afon Tarrenig

Afon Gwy
R Wye

A44

Llangurig

Llanidloes

Aberystwyth

5

A470

6 **7**

Aberystwyth

8

9

A470

10

12

11

Afon Marteg

Aberystwyth

13

14

15

Rhayader

16

A44

17

19

18

20

AQUEDUCT

21

Elan Valley B4518

Afon Elan

22

23

A470

Llanwrthwl

24

BRIDGES

1. Y Drum
2. Pont Cefn−brwyn
3. Pont Rhydgaled
4. Nanty
5. Ty−mawr
6. Glangwy
7. Llangurig
8. Pant−y−Drain
9. Dernol
10. Rhyd Dol Llech
11. Glyn Gwy
12. Marteg

13. Cwmcoch, rail (site)
14. Cwmcoch, footbridge
15. Cwmbach
16. Rhayader, Gwardolau (site)
17. Rhayader, Waun Capel Parc
18. Rhayader town bridge
19. Rhayader, Felindre
20. Ddole
21. Glyn
22. Glaslyn
23. Llanwrthwl
24. Nant−y−Craig

8 Km
5 Miles

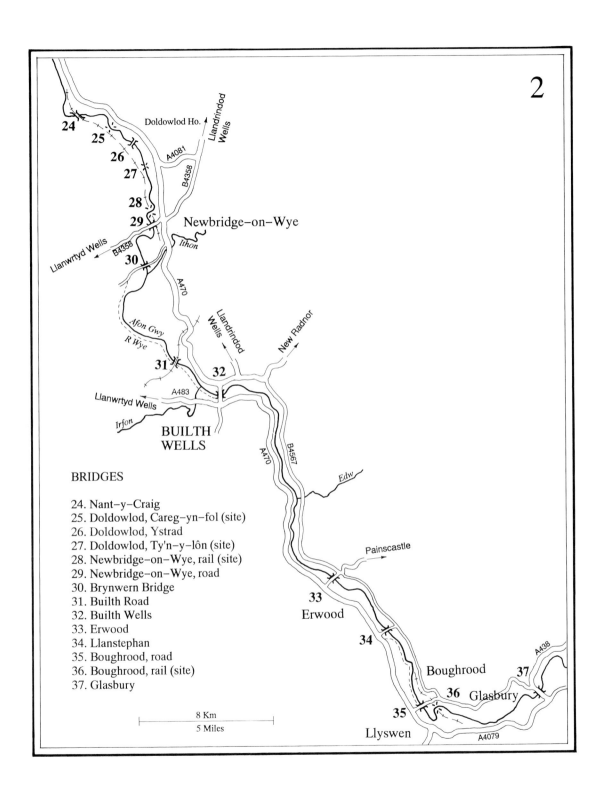

2

Doldowlod Ho.

24
25
26
27
28
29
30

Llandrindod Wells

A4081

B4358

Newbridge-on-Wye

Ithon

Llanwrtyd Wells

B4358

A470

Afon Gwy

R Wye

Llandrindod Wells

New Radnor

31
32

A483

Llanwrtyd Wells

Irfon

BUILTH
WELLS

A470

B4567

Edw

Painscastle

33
Erwood

34

Boughrood

A438

37

36 Glasbury

35

Llyswen

A4079

BRIDGES

24. Nant-y-Craig
25. Doldowlod, Careg-yn-fol (site)
26. Doldowlod, Ystrad
27. Doldowlod, Ty'n-y-lôn (site)
28. Newbridge-on-Wye, rail (site)
29. Newbridge-on-Wye, road
30. Brynwern Bridge
31. Builth Road
32. Builth Wells
33. Erwood
34. Llanstephan
35. Boughrood, road
36. Boughrood, rail (site)
37. Glasbury

8 Km
5 Miles

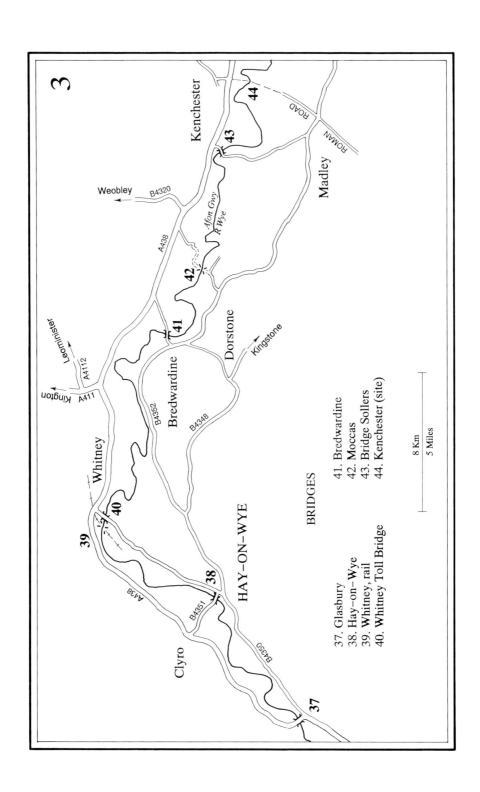

3

Kenchester

44

ROMAN ROAD

43

Madley

Weobley ← B4320

A438

Afon Gwy
R Wye

42

41

Dorstone

Kingstone ←

Leominster ↑
A4112

Kington ←
A411

Bredwardine

B4352

B4348

Whitney

40

39

38

A438

B4351

HAY–ON–WYE

Clyro

B4350

37

BRIDGES

37. Glasbury
38. Hay–on–Wye
39. Whitney, rail
40. Whitney Toll Bridge

41. Bredwardine
42. Moccas
43. Bridge Sollers
44. Kenchester (site)

8 Km
5 Miles

170

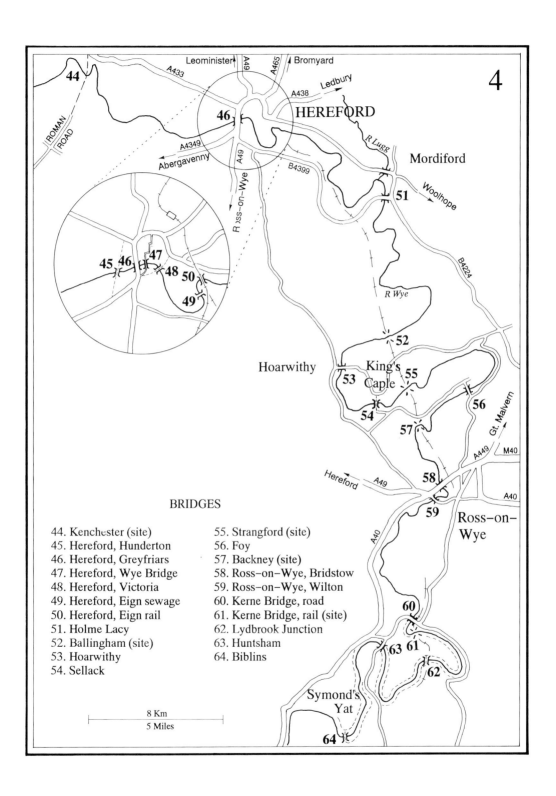

BRIDGES

44. Kenchester (site)
45. Hereford, Hunderton
46. Hereford, Greyfriars
47. Hereford, Wye Bridge
48. Hereford, Victoria
49. Hereford, Eign sewage
50. Hereford, Eign rail
51. Holme Lacy
52. Ballingham (site)
53. Hoarwithy
54. Sellack

55. Strangford (site)
56. Foy
57. Backney (site)
58. Ross-on-Wye, Bridstow
59. Ross-on-Wye, Wilton
60. Kerne Bridge, road
61. Kerne Bridge, rail (site)
62. Lydbrook Junction
63. Huntsham
64. Biblins

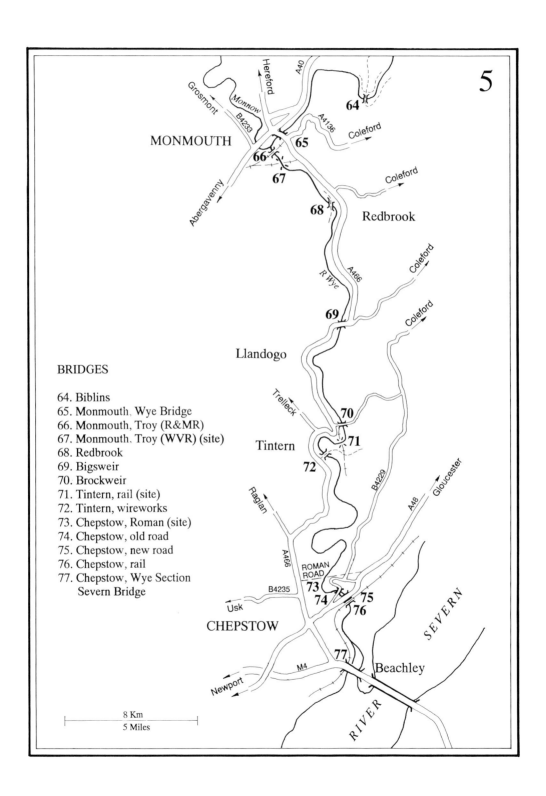

5

MONMOUTH

Redbrook

R Wye

Llandogo

Tintern

CHEPSTOW

Beachley

SEVERN

RIVER

BRIDGES

64. Biblins
65. Monmouth, Wye Bridge
66. Monmouth, Troy (R&MR)
67. Monmouth, Troy (WVR) (site)
68. Redbrook
69. Bigsweir
70. Brockweir
71. Tintern, rail (site)
72. Tintern, wireworks
73. Chepstow, Roman (site)
74. Chepstow, old road
75. Chepstow, new road
76. Chepstow, rail
77. Chepstow, Wye Section
    Severn Bridge

8 Km
5 Miles

GUIDE TO PRONUNCIATION

This does not pretend to give an accurate representation of how a Welsh person would pronounce these names, but it is a rough guide without using special phonetic symbols. It should help English speakers who find it difficult to interpret the spelling of Welsh words, as well as giving the received pronunciation of some English names which have an unusual or variable pronunciation.

Aberystwith, aber'ustwith
Boughrood, 'bochrood
Bredwardine, 'bredwardain
Brynwern, brin'wern
Builth, bilth
Caerwent, kair'went
Careg-yn-fol, karegin'vol
Cefn-Brwyn, kevn-'brooin
Cilmeri, kil'meri
Cwmbach, kum bach
Cwmcoch, kum koch
Cwmdeuddwr, kum'daithur
Cwmdewdrad, kum'diudrad
Ddole, thol
Doldowlod, dol'dowlod
Drum, drim
Eign, ain
Elan, 'elan (correct); 'eelan (acceptable)
Felindre, vel'indri
Glan Gwy, glan gui
Glanrhydgrech, glan'hreedgrech
Glasbury, 'glayzberi
Glaslyn, 'glasslin
Glyn Gwy, glin gui

Gwardolau, guar'doli
Llandrindod, hlan'drindod
Llandudno, hlan'didno
Llangurig, hlan'girig
Llanidloes, hlan'idloyss
Llanstephan, hlan'steffan
Llanwrthwl, hlan'urthul
Llanwrtyd, hlan'urtid
Llyswen, 'hleesswen
Machynlleth, mach'unhleth
Maesllwch, maiss'hluch
Nant-y-Craig, nanti'kraig
Pantmawr, pant'mowr
Pant-y-Grain, panti'grain
Pumlumon, pim'limmon
Rhayader, hrai'ader (correct);
                           'hraiader (acceptable)
Rhyd-dol-Llech, hreeddol'hlech
Rhydgaled, hreed'galed
Rhyd-hir, hreed'hir
Ty-Mawr, tee'mowr
Ty'n-y-lôn, tini'lon
Y Drum, i'drim
Ystrad, 'ustrad

KEY TO PRONUNCIATION

a	as in	bat	o	as in	pot	iu	as in due
a		car	o		bone	th	thin
ai		pine	ow		cow	th	the
ay		pain	oo		boot	ch	guttural as in loch
e		bet	oy		boy	hl	aspirated 'l'
ee		been	u		but	hr	aspirated 'r'
i		pin	u		put		

MAIN STRESSES are indicated by a mark (') placed before the relevant syllable.

SOURCES: *BBC Pronouncing Dictionary of British Names*, (Oxford, 1983); *Place names on maps of England and Wales*, (Ordnance Survey, 1981); and personal communications.